Great
TRIVIA
CHALLENGE
Quiz
Book

This edition published in 2007 by Arcturus Publishing Limited
26/27 Bickels Yard, 151–153 Bermondsey Street,
London SE1 3HA

In Canada published for Indigo Books
468 King St W,
Suite 500,
Toronto,
Ontario M5V 1L8

ISBN: 978-1-84193-826-4

Printed in China

Great TRIVIA CHALLENGE Quiz Book

Capella

Quiz 1

1 Which member of the Spice Girls released the 2001 single *Lullaby*?

2 What nationality is rugby league player Yacine Dekkiche?

3 In which year did the Police release the single *Walking on the Moon*?

4 Which country is larger in area: Albania or Belgium?

5 Which is the second largest country in South America?

6 How many months are there in the Hindu calendar?

7 Which occurred first in geological time: the Permian Period or the Cambrian Period?

8 In which city is the Islamic shrine the Kaaba?

9 With which sport are Brigitte Bécue and Agnes Kovacs associated?

10 What was the name of the character played by actress Mena Suvari in the 1999 film *American Beauty*?

Quiz 2

1 In which ocean does the country of Vanuatu lie?

2 What nationality is Formula 1 driver Marc Gené?

3 In which year were the World Indoor Athletics Championships first held?

4 In which city were the 1952 Winter Olympic Games held?

5 Which character was played by Colin Firth in the 2001 film *Bridget Jones's Diary*?

6 Which protégée of Missy Elliott recorded the 2001 album *Based on a True Story*?

7 What is the longest river in France?

8 Who directed the films *Scary Movie* and *Scary Movie 2*?

9 In which city was the International Governing Body of Fencing (the FIE) founded in 1913?

10 What would be mounted on a pan and tilt head?

Quiz 3

1 Sherwood Stewart and Ferdi Taygan won the 1982 French Open Men's Doubles Tennis Championship: which country were they from?

2 If a substance is 'caseous', what is it like?

3 What might you do with a cervelat?

4 What in Australia is known as a 'jumbuck'?

5 Which rock group released the 2001 single *All I Want*?

6 What in North American slang is a 'potsy' to a police officer?

7 In the Bible, who was the wife of Uriah?

8 What is the colour of the central stripe on the flag of Chad?

9 Which modern British city was known by the Romans as Magnus Portus?

10 Which country is home to the international governing body of gymnastics, the FIG?

Quiz 4

1 What is Elvis Presley's profession in the 1967 film *Easy Come, Easy Go*?

2 With which winter sport is the Worldloppet Cup associated?

3 In which country was cricketer Mike Procter born?

4 Physicist Niels Bohr was born and died in which European capital city?

5 Abuja is the capital of which West African republic?

6 Which country did athlete Juliet Cuthbert represent?

7 What was the registration number of Lady Penelope's pink Rolls Royce in the TV show *Thunderbirds*?

8 Des Moines is the capital of which US state?

9 Which pop singer originally had a No 1 single with the song *When the Going Gets Tough, the Tough Get Going*?

10 Which river flows into the North Sea at Sunderland?

Quiz 5

1 What nationality is weightlifter Li Feng-Ying?

2 The magician Drosselmeyer is a character in which ballet by Tchaikovsky?

3 What is Kim Basinger's character's name in the 1997 film *LA Confidential*?

4 In which city was guitarist Jimi Hendrix born?

5 In which month is the Kentucky Derby run in the USA?

6 Which group did Ian Astbury form following the split of The Cult in 1995?

7 Who produced the *Tom and Jerry* cartoons?

8 On which Caribbean island is the volcano Mount Pelee?

9 What type of foodstuff is a red savina Habanero?

10 Which plant is the source of tequila?

Quiz 6

1 Which letter was transmitted in Morse code from Cornwall to Newfoundland in 1901, to the radio pioneer Marconi?

2 What are sevruga, beluga and ascieta?

3 Of which country was Tomas Masaryk president from 1918 to 1935?

4 Which member of the Beatles played bass guitar?

5 Which supermodel became Joey's roommate in the comedy series *Friends*?

6 Which female vocalist in collaboration with ELO had a 1980 UK No 1 with *Xanadu*?

7 In which English county is the Fylingdales early warning radar station?

8 Which is the longest river in Northern Ireland?

9 Which tennis player penned the 1985 autobiography entitled *Being Myself*?

10 Which happened first in geological time: the Jurassic or Silurian Period?

Quiz 7

1 In which year did Marilyn Monroe die, aged 36?

2 How many months are there in the Sikh calendar?

3 Who founded the city of Quebec in 1608?

4 Which country lies between Estonia and Lithuania?

5 Which film actress did the tennis player John McEnroe marry in 1986?

6 Which 2000 film saw Arnold Schwarzenegger coming face to face with his clone?

7 In which European country is the ski resort of Madonna di Campiglio?

8 From which English city would a Brummie come?

9 Which city is the setting for the 1957 film *The Prince and the Showgirl*?

10 Who wrote the novel *About a Boy*, which was adapted into a 2002 film starring Hugh Grant?

Quiz 8

1 At which sport did Iain Percy win a gold medal at the 2000 Olympics?

2 Which shipping forecast area lies immediately east of Forties?

3 Which 1953 film starring Marilyn Monroe and Jane Russell featured the song *Diamonds are a Girl's Best Friend*?

4 Which former US president wrote the 1985 book *No More Vietnams*?

5 What is the name by which members of the Unification Church are more commonly known?

6 What is the average gestation period (in days) of a horse?

7 Which Chinese province was invaded by Japan in 1931 and not relinquished until 1945?

8 In which religion is the Beth Din the court of judgment?

9 Which letter of the Greek alphabet is the equivalent of the letter 'Z'?

10 Which US state is larger in area: Arizona or Colorado?

Quiz 9

1 Which sea was known to the Romans as Mare Internum?

2 Which sport was invented by James Naismith in 1891?

3 What fabric covers a snooker table?

4 Shinty is a form of which sport?

5 Which book of the Bible has more chapters: Jeremiah or Job?

6 In which sport does a hooter sound at the end of the game?

7 What is the capital of Norway?

8 Which scientist wrote *A Brief History of Time*?

9 Which author introduced the word 'robot' into the modern vocabulary?

10 What was the first name of the 19th century English cookery writer, Mrs Beeton?

Quiz 10

1 In which century did the Crimean War take place?

2 In which US state is the city of Tallahassee?

3 Which sport is central to the film *Escape to Victory*?

4 What nationality was the composer Antonin Dvorak?

5 Which pop star was born Harry Rodger Webb?

6 In which film did Arnold Schwarzenegger first star as a cyborg?

7 What is the capital of Queensland, Australia?

8 What is the official language of Mexico?

9 What is the standard monetary unit of Turkey?

10 Who wrote the poem *Death Be Not Proud*?

Quiz 11

1 Who wrote *Bleak House*?

2 Which actor's real name was Marion Michael Morrison?

3 What would a costermonger sell?

4 Which actress played the title rôle in the film adaptation of *Bridget Jones's Diary*?

5 'George' is an informal name for which feature of an aircraft?

6 Who wrote *The Loneliness of the Long Distance Runner*?

7 How is Sarah Michelle Gellar better known to millions?

8 Ganymede is a satellite of which planet?

9 What nationality was the composer Wolfgang Amadeus Mozart?

10 For which element is Co the chemical symbol?

Quiz 12

1 Which beloved and accomplished Canadian author wrote *The Stone Angel* and *Dance on the Earth*?

2 Who followed William Taft as US president?

3 Which actor was born Archibald Alexander Leach?

4 Which of these birds (if any) can fly: kookaburra, ostrich, kiwi, cassowary?

5 Who have Robert Donat, Kenneth More and Robert Powell all played on film?

6 What was the name of the daughter of Samantha and Darrin in *Bewitched*?

7 Which D H Lawrence novel concerns several generations of the Brangwen family?

8 Aconcagua is the highest peak in which mountain chain?

9 Of what is cyberphobia the irrational fear?

10 The adjective 'vulpine' relates to which family of animals?

Quiz 13

1 What was the name of the boy who befriended ET in the film of that name?

2 Of what is Roquefort a type?

3 Who was president of the USA from 1963 to 1969?

4 The song *White Christmas* comes from which film?

5 What is the capital of Paraguay?

6 What is the chemical symbol for gold?

7 Which US film composer won Oscars for his work on *Breakfast at Tiffany's* and *Victor/Victoria*?

8 Which actor said "I have played three presidents, three saints and two geniuses: if that doesn't create an ego problem, nothing does"?

9 What nationality was the explorer Mungo Park?

10 What is a clavicord?

Quiz 14

1 Is the meerkat diurnal or nocturnal?

2 The Sierra Madre chain is the main mountain system of which country?

3 As what was the Russian Anna Pavlova best known?

4 In which century was Sir Isaac Newton born?

5 Where are the Islets of Langerhans?

6 Which sea strait links the Mediterranean Sea with the Atlantic Ocean?

7 In which US city was John F Kennedy assassinated in 1963?

8 The French port of Saint Nazaire stands at the mouth of which river?

9 At which sport have Eirik Kvalfoss and Frank Ullrich been world champions?

10 In which city was country music star Kenny Rogers born?

Quiz 15

1 Which singing artist fronted The Commodores for 12 years before going solo in 1982?

2 At which racecourse is the English Grand National run?

3 The port of Salto is the second largest city of which South American country?

4 Which Finn was the 1998 Australian Formula 1 Grand Prix winner?

5 In which US state is the Kilauea volcano?

6 Of which country is Funafuti the capital?

7 In which African country are the Karuru and Gura waterfalls?

8 Which animal represents the year 2008 in the Chinese calendar?

9 On which Mediterranean island is the author Robert Graves buried?

10 In which opera by Rimsky Korsakov does King Dodon appear?

Quiz 16

1 What nationality was the sprinter Ray Stewart?

2 *Fat of the Land,* which went straight to No 1 in the US album charts in 1997, was by which band?

3 Which Frenchman made the first flight across the English Channel in 1909?

4 Who was the goddess of youth and spring in Greek mythology?

5 Which city in central India was the site of a poisonous gas leak in 1984?

6 …and which company was responsible for this disaster?

7 Which Norwegian painter's works include *The Scream*?

8 What nationality is the tenor Giuseppe Di Stefano?

9 What nationality was Olympic shooting champion Gudbrand Skatteboe?

10 If something is 'clavate' what shape is it?

Quiz 17

1 Which Canadian songstress whose albums include *The Best Damn Thing* and *Under My Skin* had a smash hit in 2007 with *Girlfriend*?

2 What length of imprisonment is implied by the term 'double sawbuck' in the US?

3 Who was a Best Actor Oscar winner for the film *Scent of a Woman*?

4 Who was the composer of the oratorio *The Dream of Gerontius*?

5 How old was Andre Agassi when he first won a Wimbledon Singles title?

6 What in computer science is OCR?

7 Which company originally developed the computer mouse?

8 What nationality is tennis player Lleyton Hewitt?

9 What nationality is skier Bente Martinsen?

10 In 1999, Michael J Fox announced that he was suffering from which illness?

Quiz 18

1 Who was married to actress Ali McGraw from 1973 to 1978?

2 Kym Marsh was the first member to leave which manufactured pop group?

3 Who wrote the books which were adapted for the TV series *Jeeves and Wooster*?

4 Who created the character Chief Inspector Roderick Alleyn?

5 How many white stars are on the national flag of the USA?

6 In the film *The Hunt for Red October*, in which ocean does the action take place?

7 A howdah is a seat used for riding on the back of which animal?

8 What is another term for lockjaw?

9 What is the name of the family featured in the John Ford film *The Grapes of Wrath*?

10 What nationality was the composer Edward Elgar?

ANSWERS:
1 Steve McQueen, 2 Hear'Say, 3 P G Wodehouse, 4 Ngaio Marsh, 5 50,
6 Atlantic, 7 Elephant, 8 Tetanus, 9 Joad, 10 English.

Quiz 19

1 For which country did the cricketer Sunil Gavaskar play?

2 Jean Valjean is the hero of which novel, which was turned into a musical by Andrew Lloyd Webber?

3 What is the standard monetary unit of Spain?

4 Who wrote the children's book *The Wind in the Willows*?

5 What is the meaning of the word 'moribund'?

6 What was the surname of the Little Women in the book of the same name by Louisa M Alcott?

7 What is the first name of Gulliver in the book *Gulliver's Travels* by Jonathan Swift?

8 What is the medical name for the human thighbone?

9 Who was the sweetheart of Yogi Bear in the cartoon series?

10 Yellowstone National Park covers three US states: Montana and Idaho are two, which is the third?

Quiz 20

1 Only four US states have a common meeting point: Colorado and Arizona are two of these, which are the other two?

2 Which US state has borders with Wyoming, South Dakota, Iowa, Kansas, Colorado and Missouri?

3 The soap opera *Knott's Landing* was a spin-off from which other US soap?

4 Who directed the 1941 film *Citizen Kane*?

5 What is the capital of the principality of Wales?

6 What was the name of the anti-war book by Erich Maria Remarque which was twice made into a film?

7 What nationality was the legendary motor racing driver Juan Manuel Fangio?

8 In 1987, Stephen Roche become the first Irishman to win what?

9 Who was the first British golfer to win the US Masters title?

10 Jose Napoles and John H Stracey are former champions of which sport?

Quiz 21

1 Name the Edinburgh-born inventor of the telephone who emigrated to Canada in 1870.

2 Which *Star Trek* film has the subtitle *The Voyage Home*?

3 Richard Hadlee and Dennis Lillee are former players of which sport?

4 The bacterial disease glanders can be passed on to humans from which animal?

5 In which novel by Charles Dickens does Captain Cuttle appear?

6 Which composer is associated with the film *The Sting*?

7 To which house does Harry Potter belong in the novels by J K Rowling?

8 Pulque is a light alcoholic drink which comes from which country?

9 Which James Bond film was the last to use a title actually written by Ian Fleming?

10 Who directed the 1993 film *Schindler's List*?

Quiz 22

1 Which is Australia's largest city by population?

2 A rickshaw would typically be used as a form of transport in parts of which continent?

3 Who wrote the whodunnit novel *The Murder of Roger Ackroyd*?

4 What was the first name of Sigourney Weaver's character Ripley in the *Alien* films?

5 How many minutes are there in one day?

6 Which US city is nicknamed 'The Windy City'?

7 What is the twelfth sign of the zodiac?

8 What sort of animal is Snowball in George Orwell's *Animal Farm*?

9 *Take My Breath Away* was the 1986 Oscar-winning song from which film?

10 What was the name of the car in the film *The Lovebug*?

Quiz 23

1 What pen-name does J K Rowling use as the author of *Fantastic Beasts and Where to Find Them*?

2 Children's TV favourite Pingu was created in which country?

3 A griffin has the body of which animal?

4 Who was the first wife of King Henry VIII of England?

5 Who created the detective Sam Spade?

6 What is another name for the atmospheric phenomenon *aurora borealis*?

7 In which US state is the hi-tech industrial region known as Silicon Valley?

8 On television, who regarded himself as being "smarter than the average bear"?

9 In which war did the Battle of Leyte Gulf take place?

10 Which legendary US vocalist had a top five single in 1969 with *Lay Lady Lay*?

Quiz 24

1 In which Scottish city is the University of Strathclyde?

2 Which country was known by the Romans as Lusitania?

3 Rickets is a disease caused by a deficiency of which vitamin?

4 From which country was the seventh Secretary General of the United Nations, Kofi Annan?

5 ...and what was the nationality of his successor, Ban Ki-moon?

6 In which European country might one be awarded The Order of the Elephant?

7 SK is the abbreviation of which Canadian province?

8 In which US city is the Henry Ford Museum?

9 In which decade of the 20th century did Japan join the United Nations?

10 Which boxer was known as 'The Brown Bomber'?

Quiz 25

1 Which Canadian TV personality is the popular quizmaster of *Jeopardy*?

2 Which book of the Bible has more chapters: Exodus or Genesis?

3 Of what does a bibliophile have a love?

4 Which US state is the largest in area: Connecticut, Hawaii or Nebraska?

5 The disease scurvy occurs as a result of which vitamin deficiency?

6 Which material is traditionally associated with a thirteenth wedding anniversary?

7 Who wrote the science fiction classic novel *I, Robot*?

8 In which US state was the athlete Jesse Owens born?

9 Which 1989 baseball film featured Tom Berenger and Charlie Sheen as team-mates?

10 In computing, what does the abbreviation GIF stand for?

Quiz 26

1 Which ocean is the larger: the Indian Ocean or the Atlantic Ocean?

2 Which European city was known to the Romans as Olisipo?

3 How much did Nokia's first mobile phone, the Mobira Senator, weigh when it was introduced in 1982, 1.7 kg or 9.8 kg?

4 What is the nickname given to Schubert's *Quintet in A Major*?

5 What type of creature is a wels?

6 What is the average gestation period of an African elephant: 26 weeks or 91 weeks?

7 AF is the two-letter code for which major European airline?

8 In a car, what is ABS?

9 What colour is the crown of a green woodpecker?

10 Of which country did Silvio Berlusconi become prime minister in 2001?

Quiz 27

1 Which book of the Bible has more chapters: Jonah or Micah?

2 In heraldry, if an animal is sejant, how is it represented?

3 Which is the smallest European owl?

4 Which controversial rap star appeared at the 2001 Brit Awards with a mask and chainsaw?

5 Which anarchic punk band had a UK top 5 hit in 1977 with *God Save the Queen*?

6 What type of animal is the emperor turned into in the 2000 Disney film *The Emperor's New Groove*?

7 In Sikhism, what is a kara?

8 In the Bible, who was the sixth son of Jacob?

9 In which European country might one find a spectacled salamander?

10 In which South American country is the Itatinga waterfall?

ANSWERS:
1 Jonah, 2 Sitting, 3 Pigmy owl, 4 Eminem, 5 The Sex Pistols, 6 A llama,
7 A bangle, 8 Naphtali, 9 Italy, 10 Brazil.

Quiz 28

1 Of what is chrystallophobia the fear: crystals or the colour green?

2 Which football team won the first UK FA Cup final at the new Wembley Stadium, in 2007?

3 Of what is doraphobia the fear?

4 Which country administers the Queen Charlotte Islands?

5 How many digits has a bear on each foot?

6 In which group of UK islands would one find Tresco and St Mary's?

7 Which country was called Dania by the Romans?

8 Which book of the Bible has more chapters: Esther or Ruth?

9 Which international organization goes by the acronym CARICOM?

10 What is the average gestation period of a camel: 28 weeks or 58 weeks?

Quiz 29

1 Which substance is associated with a 14th wedding anniversary?

2 In which country is the Batmanhole Cave?

3 What nationality was chemist and philanthropist Alfred Nobel?

4 What was Kirsty Alley's character's name in the hugely popular sitcom *Cheers*?

5 What nationality is golfer Jarrod Moseley?

6 Which team signed Canadian ice hockey player Marc Hussey in August 1999?

7 Which jazz guitarist died in December 1999 at the age of 74?

8 Which female singer had a 2000 No 1 hit with *Born to make You Happy*?

9 In Greek mythology, which of the three Fates was the Spinner of the Thread of Life?

10 Mount Smolikas is the highest peak in which Greek mountain range?

Quiz 30

1 Who did Hervé Villechaize play in the Bond film *The Man With the Golden Gun*?

2 The Swaythling Cup is competed for in which sport?

3 São Miguel is the largest of which group of Atlantic islands belonging to Portugal?

4 Honshu and Hokkaido are two of the main islands of which country?

5 Which girl group had a 2000 No 1 single with the song *Black Coffee*?

6 In snooker, how many points is the green ball worth?

7 Who drove the Ring-a-Ding Convert-a-Car in the cartoon series *Wacky Races*?

8 What nationality is canoeist Renn Crichlow?

9 Which solo artiste had a 1999 Top Ten single with *Waiting for Tonight*?

10 Olof Palme first became prime minister of which country in 1969?

Quiz 31

1 Which Canadian journalist anchored the ABC *World News Tonight* for over 20 years?

2 Who wrote the novel *Life and Loves of a She Devil*?

3 In which country was shipping magnate Aristotle Onassis born?

4 Who played Angel in a television spin-off series from the show *Buffy the Vampire Slayer*?

5 For which sport is the Espirito Santo Trophy awarded?

6 Louping ill is a disease of which animal?

7 In ancient Egypt, what would a canopic jar have contained?

8 In zoology, if something is acaudal, what does it lack?

9 In which gambling game is the phrase 'a cheval' used?

10 Which chesspiece makes L-shaped moves?

Quiz 32

1 Of which US state is Boise the capital?

2 What is Eddie Murphy's character's name in the 1996 film *The Nutty Professor*?

3 With which sport would you associate the name of Michael Hadschieff and Ye Qiaobo?

4 Which sport do the Canterbury Crusaders and Auckland Blues play in New Zealand?

5 In which sport might the Sheffield Sharks play the Chester Jets?

6 Which rapper recorded the 2000 album *Roc La Familia*?

7 In which European country was the Nobel prizewinning chemist A I Virtanen born?

8 Which of these is not a prime number: 547, 557 or 567?

9 For what was Otto Hahn awarded the 1944 Nobel Prize in Chemistry?

10 Which US food manufacturer invented the advertising slogan '57 Varieties'?

Quiz 33

1 Who wrote the 1978 novel *The Sea, the Sea*?

2 Which imaginary creature is depicted as white horse with one spiralled horn growing from its forehead?

3 At which sport is Australian Kieran Perkins a former world champion?

4 In which sport is the James Norris Memorial Trophy awarded?

5 In which city is the US football team The Carolina Panthers based?

6 Which famous UK fashion designer married Andreas Kronthaler in 1992?

7 In 1996, which female singer famously attacked a reporter at Bangkok airport?

8 How old was reggae legend Bob Marley when he died: 36 or 42?

9 What was the name of Mel Gibson's character in the *Lethal Weapon* films?

10 What was the nationality of the character played by Ralph Fiennes in *The English Patient*?

Quiz 34

1 In February 2005, which renowned Canadian short story writer was awarded the Medal of Honor for Literature from the USA National Arts Club?

2 In which game is a flat stone bounced across the surface of water?

3 Who was represented in Greek mythology as wearing winged sandals?

4 What is the common name for pyrites or iron pyrites?

5 What name is given to the permanent freezing of the ground in areas bordering on ice sheets?

6 What is the capital of Indonesia?

7 Which German composer wrote the opera *Der Rosenkavalier*?

8 In which country is the port of Jaffna?

9 What was the name of the official bodyguard of Roman emperors, created by Augustus?

10 Which archangel announced the birth of John the Baptist to Zechariah?

Quiz 35

1 Which British novelist penned *Mansfield Park* and *Northanger Abbey*?

2 In which London church is Poets' Corner?

3 What was the debut single of the Pet Shop Boys, which hit the UK No 1 spot in 1985?

4 Which legendary actor and dancer's first screen appearance came in 1933's *Dancing Lady*, in which he played himself?

5 Which 1973 film featured Jack Nicholson as a sailor escorting a thief to naval prison?

6 Which African country was formerly known as Dahomey?

7 In which Sheridan play does the character Mrs Malaprop appear?

8 Which German driver achieved his first Formula 1 victory in the 2001 San Marino Grand Prix?

9 Which is the largest of the United Arab Emirates?

10 Dagestan is an autonomous republic of which country?

Quiz 36

1 Who was the first murder victim in the Bible?

2 What was the name of the Lone Ranger's Indian companion?

3 *The Lone Ranger* TV theme music comes from which Rossini opera?

4 Which Australian city is named after the queen consort of King William IV of England?

5 What was the profession of the character played by Jack Nicholson in *Terms of Endearment*?

6 By what name was the only English pope, Nicholas Brakespear known?

7 Who was the sixth president of the USA?

8 Margaret Dumont was the long-suffering stooge to which comedy team?

9 Which sea lies between the Italian mainland and the islands of Sicily, Sardinia and Corsica?

10 What nationality is the actress Liv Ullmann?

Quiz 37

1 Which Canadian filmmaker has a cult following, with films such as *The Fly*, *Scanners* and *Videodrome*?

2 What name is given to a Muslim place of worship?

3 Which is the only venomous snake found wild in the British Isles?

4 In the summer of 2000, which cricket side was beaten by England in a Test series for the first time in 31 years?

5 What is the weight division applied to a professional boxer who weighs between 112 and 118 pounds?

6 What is the maximum length (in inches) of a baseball bat?

7 In which sport do England and Scotland compete for the Calcutta Cup?

8 What colour ring on an archery target is worth seven points?

9 What is the stage name of Marshall Bruce Mathers III?

10 With which singing group did Diana Ross find fame?

Quiz 38

1 Which US author created the detective Philip Marlowe?

2 What name is given to a boundary between air masses which have a different temperature and humidity?

3 According to legend, at whom did Peeping Tom peep?

4 Which Irish monk founded the famous monastery at Lindisfarne off the coast of Northumberland, England?

5 What is the name of the cat in *The Simpsons*?

6 In the Old Testament, who was the twin brother of Jacob?

7 How many heads of US presidents are carved into Mount Rushmore?

8 Who replaced Peter Gabriel as the lead singer of Genesis in 1975?

9 Of which African country is Lusaka the capital?

10 Which actor starred as advertising executive Nick Marshall in the 2000 film *What Women Want*?

Quiz 41

1 Which British king abdicated in 1936?

2 Which veteran singer-songwriter won the award for Best Original Song at the 2001 Oscars?

3 With what sort of books is author Louis L'Amour chiefly associated?

4 With which sport is Kareem Abdul-Jabbar associated?

5 Who wrote the book *The Cat in the Hat*?

6 Which Shakespeare play features Ferdinand, the King of Navarre?

7 Which community for homeless boys was founded by Father Edward Flanagan in Nebraska in 1917?

8 What was the pen-name of the author John Griffith Chaney?

9 Abigail was one of the wives of which Biblical king of Israel?

10 By what name is the central keep of the Tower of London known?

Quiz 42

1 Which ship, a major London tourist attraction, was damaged by fire on the morning of 21 May 2007?

2 Is a culverin a type of weapon or a type of drainpipe?

3 Which British author created the detective Albert Campion?

4 Which comic strip features Snoopy, Charlie Brown and Linus?

5 The adjective 'lupine' relates to which family of animals?

6 In which European country is the port of La Coruña?

7 Which athletics field event was formerly known as the 'hop, step and jump'?

8 To which film was *The Jewel of the Nile* a sequel?

9 Which Italian actor starred in *A Fistful of Dollars* and *Lucky Luciano*?

10 What relation was novelist Isabel Allende to the overthrown Chilean president Salvador Allende?

Quiz 45

1 Which Canadian singer recorded the albums *Blue* and *Miles of Aisles*?

2 Which device in a jet engine provides extra thrust for take-off or supersonic flight?

3 The film *Jerry Maguire* featured which sport?

4 What is the chief river of Ghana?

5 Which 2001 film about the Cuban missile crisis starred Kevin Costner?

6 Which epic poem by Dante begins on Good Friday in the year 1300?

7 Which German motor manufacturer was set up in 1937 to produce a 'people's car'?

8 The River Tamar forms a historic boundary between which two English counties?

9 Who played Sally Bowles in the film *Cabaret*?

10 Which fish is smoked and sold as finnan haddie?

Quiz 46

1 Which city in Switzerland was the headquarters of the League of Nations?

2 At which sport have Keiji, Okada and Yuko Hasama been world champions?

3 Which man set a world record of 10.2 seconds for the 100 metres sprint on 20 June 1936?

4 Who wrote the novel *The Fourth Protocol*?

5 Ljubljana is the capital of which republic of central Europe?

6 Which boardgame was invented by Alfred M Butts?

7 What is Kim Basinger's profession in the 1987 film *Nadine*?

8 In which US state is the port of Tarpon Springs?

9 In which European country is the ski resort of Obergurgl?

10 The Whit Sunday Islands lie off the coast of which Australian state?

Quiz 47

1 The Zugspitze is the highest mountain of which European country?

2 What is the name of the female reproductive part of a flower?

3 What is the name given to the mass of lympoid tissue at the back of the throat behind the uvula?

4 In which Italian city is the famous La Scala Opera House?

5 Which Phoenician prince in Greek mythology slew the dragon guarding the Spring of Ares?

6 The Monte Rosa Massif stands on the borders of which European countries?

7 Which winter sport are Anton Fischer and Jeffrey Jost associated?

8 Which sport is played by the New Jersey Devils?

9 What nationality is golfer Colleen Walker?

10 Which female singer had a 1983 Top Ten hit with the song *Move Over Darling*?

Quiz 48

1 Who was elected vice president of the USA in 1852, but died six weeks after being sworn in?

2 Who became president of Egypt in 1981?

3 The War of the Bavarian Succession was fought between which two countries?

4 In martial arts, what is an ashi gatami?

5 What is the name of Woody's horse in the film *Toy Story 2*?

6 In which field event would you associate Philippa Roles and Judy Oakes?

7 In which sport were Ichiro Ogimura and Yoshio Tomita world champions in 1956?

8 What nationality was skier Christl Cranz?

9 In which Australian city is the Albert Park Formula 1 motor racing circuit?

10 What is dactylography?

Quiz 49

1 In 1992, which Canadian baseball team became the first non-US team to win baseball's coveted World Series?

2 In North American slang, what is a 'sky bear'?

3 Which bird makes its first appearance on the seventh day of Christmas in the song *The Twelve Days of Christmas*?

4 What type of creature is a 'nilgai'?

5 Which island of the Mediterranean Sea is separated from Italy by the Straits of Messina?

6 What is 'lincrusta'?

7 What might you do in East Africa if you had a 'kanzu'?

8 Which comedian thinks he has only two weeks to live in the 1939 comedy *Never Say Die*?

9 Which city is the setting for the 1973 film *The Sting*?

10 What nationality was WBC Super Featherweight Boxing Champion Cornelius Boza Edwards?

Quiz 50

1 Which female singer recorded the 1999 album *Telegram*?

2 What does MS-DOS stand for in computing?

3 Of which planet is Desdemona a satellite?

4 Which element did Otto Hahn and Lise Meitner discover in 1918?

5 What colour is pitchblende?

6 Which actor voiced the Genie in the 1992 animated film *Aladdin*?

7 Actress Kate Hudson is the daughter of which other actress?

8 Who did the singer Jennifer Lopez marry in 2001?

9 Who starred as the psychiatrist in the 1992 film *Final Analysis*?

10 Which gas forms a larger percentage of the air by volume: ozone or neon?

Quiz 51

1 In which city was the mime artiste Marcel Marceau born?

2 In which Asian country is the city of Niigata?

3 What type of performer is an 'ecdysiast'?

4 Which African country lies immediately west of Botswana?

5 Which island is larger: Java or Hispaniola?

6 The adjective 'hepatic' refers to which of the five senses?

7 On which of the Hawaiian islands is Mount Tantalus?

8 What are the constituent elements of the alloy solder?

9 In which sport might you perform a 'septime'?

10 Which countries fought in the Battle of Rocroi in 1643?

Quiz 52

1 For what is the word 'lea' a poetic term?

2 Who plays comic-book expert Elijah Price in the 2000 film *Unbreakable*?

3 Which flamboyant singer reached the UK No 1 spot posthumously in 1993 with *Living on My Own*?

4 In which sport was the father of Grace Kelly an Olympic gold medallist?

5 Who was the first US racing driver to win the Formula 1 World Championship?

6 Which British administrator originated the penny postage system?

7 In which film did Humphrey Bogart play the character of Charlie Allnut?

8 By what name is Mendelssohn's Fourth Symphony known?

9 Of which former Soviet state is Bishkek the capital?

10 By what name is the 16th century astrologer Michelle de Notredame known?

Quiz 53

1 Which letter of the Greek alphabet is the equivalent of the letter 'K'?

2 What is the meaning of the common abbreviation CD-ROM?

3 Which period of geological time saw the appearance of humans?

4 Which Texas town was established in 1849 to protect settlers from attacks by the Comanche tribe?

5 MB is the abbreviation of which Canadian province?

6 What is the average gestation period of a lion: 15 weeks or 26 weeks?

7 Who penned the poem *The Village Blacksmith*?

8 In which European capital city is the grave of the Doors singer Jim Morrison?

9 Which *Four Weddings and a Funeral* star played Clive Durham in the 1987 film *Maurice*?

10 What is the correct form of spoken address to a pope?

Quiz 54

1 In computing, what does the abbreviation LSI stand for?

2 From which country was the sixth Secretary General of the United Nations, Boutros Boutros-Ghali?

3 What is the meaning of the common abbreviation BAFTA?

4 What is the colour of the cross on the flag of Finland?

5 In which year did Boris Becker first play Stefan Edberg in the Wimbledon Men's Singles Tennis Championship?

6 In which year did the Nuremberg Trials begin?

7 Which island is further north: Ibiza or Minorca?

8 Name one of the five British Foreign Secretaries who served under Mrs Thatcher.

9 Which battle initiated the Wars of the Roses in 1455?

10 In which state of the USA is the city of Amarillo?

Quiz 55

1 Which chart-topping Canadian country singer released her mega album *Up!* in 2002?

2 Which of Batman's enemies was portrayed on the small screen by Burgess Meredith?

3 Who played the assassin hired to kill President De Gaulle in the 1973 film *The Day of the Jackal*?

4 Which European city is further west: Genoa or Munich?

5 In which city is the headquarters of the UN agency The International Labour Organisation?

6 In heraldry, if an animal is rampant, how is it represented?

7 In martial arts, what is a 'hanbo'?

8 Which German city is further west: Bonn or Düsseldorf?

9 Who was the author of the novel *The Mayor of Casterbridge*?

10 In US slang what is an 'ambulance chaser'?

Quiz 56

1 Of which country is Douala the capital?

2 What is the official language of the Central American country El Salvador?

3 In which US city is the Everson Museum of Art?

4 Which substance is usually associated with a 15th wedding anniversary?

5 Which Hollywood actor provided the voice of Rocky the Rooster in the animated film *Chicken Run*?

6 Who wrote the novels *Jamaica Inn* and *Rebecca*?

7 What type of creature is a 'moderlieschen'?

8 What is the collective noun for locusts?

9 In which country are the Ilopango and Izalco volcanoes?

10 Which poet's volumes include 1899's *The Wind Amongst the Reeds*?

Quiz 57

1 On which bay is the Spanish port of Bilbao?

2 Of what is clinophobia a fear?

3 In which year were the Summer Olympic Games held in Seoul?

4 Which US born British sculptor created *The Rock Drill* and *St Michael and the Devil*?

5 What was the name given to the tax levied in Anglo-Saxon Britain to buy off Viking invaders?

6 Who wrote the novel *Mr Midshipman Easy*?

7 In which US city were the 1984 Summer Olympics held?

8 Which film first made a star of juvenile actor Macaulay Culkin?

9 Who was the first man to be mentioned in the Bible?

10 On which river does the German city of Ulm stand?

Quiz 58

1 Of which US city was Richard Daley the mayor from 1955-1976?

2 Which Italian dictator was known as Il Duce?

3 Which Mel Brooks film featured the song *Springtime for Hitler*?

4 Of which rock group was Francis Rossi lead singer?

5 In which century was the diary of Samuel Pepys first published?

6 Who wrote the novels *Tropic of Capricorn* and *Tropic of Cancer*?

7 Which 2001 film starred Keanu Reeves, James Spader and Marisa Tomei?

8 What name is given to the mark under the 'c' in words such as façade and Française?

9 Which very hard metal has the chemical symbol Ta?

10 Who was allowed to help Jesus to carry the cross to his crucifixion?

Quiz 59

1 How many years are there in one century?

2 The former duchy of Brabant is divided between which two present-day European states?

3 After appearing together in which film did Tom Hanks and Rita Wilson decide to marry?

4 Which French painter, together with Pablo Picasso founded Cubism?

5 What sort of creature is a 'trogon'?

6 In the *Stations of the Cross*, what number is the picture in which Jesus dies on the cross?

7 What name is given to a Hindu of the highest caste?

8 By what name is nacre popularly known?

9 In which 2000 film did Johnny Depp appear as a gypsy called Cesar?

10 Which 2000 film starring Val Kilmer was based around an expedition to Mars?

Quiz 60

1 From what condition does Dustin Hoffman's character suffer in the 1988 film *Rain Man*?

2 Which state unilaterally declared independence from Nigeria in 1967?

3 Which atoll in the Marshall Islands gave its name to a form of swimwear?

4 Which joint is formed by the meeting of the humerus, radius and ulna?

5 Which actor plays William Forrester in the film *Finding Forrester*?

6 Of which US state is Frankfort the capital?

7 Which English novelist wrote *The Children of the New Forest*?

8 Which was the first Sunday newspaper to be published in Britain?

9 *Let the River Run* was the 1988 Oscar-winning song from which film?

10 The film *The Claim* is based on which Thomas Hardy novel?

Quiz 61

1 Which eccentric Canadian classical pianist was considered by many to be the world's finest interpreter of Bach?

2 Which fibrous protein is found in hair, nails, horns, hooves and skin?

3 Which chemical element has the symbol Se?

4 Which member of the Kennedy family drove his car off a bridge in 1969?

5 In February 2001, which glamourous Hollywood couple announced their separation after 11 years of marriage?

6 What nationality was the one member of Abba who was not Swedish?

7 Which singer was billed as The Last of the Red-Hot Mammas?

8 Which 2000 film featuring David Arquette and Oliver Platt was set in the world of wrestling?

9 In which novel by Jane Austen is Anne Elliot the heroine?

10 In which New York City borough are Wall Street and Broadway?

Quiz 62

1 What was the name of the bear on television's *The Life and Times of Grizzly Adams*?

2 Which former Wimbledon champion died of AIDS in 1993?

3 Which Japanese detective did Peter Lorre play in a series of films?

4 In which US state is Kent State University?

5 What was the first name of FBI agent Starling in the films *Silence of the Lambs* and *Hannibal*?

6 Which Disney film features the voices of John Goodman and Eartha Kitt?

7 Which prayer is also called paternoster or Our Father?

8 Marie Byrd Land is an unclaimed region of which continent?

9 In which year was the siege at the mission in San Antonio, Texas, popularly called the Alamo?

10 Which country was formerly known as Siam?

Quiz 63

1 Who directed the 1981 film *Raiders of the Lost Ark*?

2 Which city is the capital of Northern Ireland?

3 What is the name given to chisel-edged teeth at the front of the mouth?

4 Who is the suitor of Bianca in Shakespeare's *The Taming of the Shrew*?

5 In which country was the television series *Xena: Warrior Princess* filmed?

6 Which former actress in the television soap *Dallas* appeared on the London stage as Mrs Robinson in a 2001 production of *The Graduate*?

7 In which sport would you encounter the terms 'ballet', 'moguls' and 'aerials'?

8 Of which country is Vilnius the capital?

9 On which Mediterranean island are the towns of Malia and Sitia?

10 Walachia is a region of which European country?

Quiz 64

1 In which Canadian province might you ski at the Kicking Horse Mountain Resort?

2 On which of the Great Lakes is the Michigan port of St Joseph?

3 On which European island are the ruins of Agrigento to be found?

4 Where would an Edwardian woman have worn a toque?

5 Which singer starred in the 1957 film *Jailhouse Rock*?

6 Who won a Best Actor Oscar for his part in the film *The Godfather*?

7 The heavy woollen cloth known as duffel is named after a town in which European country?

8 What is the name of the God of Thunder in Wagner's opera *Das Rheingold*?

9 Which Andrew Lloyd Webber musical closed on Broadway in 2001 after more than 7,000 performances?

10 Which boxer plays himself in the film *Black and White* during which he beats up Robert Downey Jr?

Quiz 65

1. Which actress plays the stalker of Clint Eastwood in the 1971 film *Play Misty for Me*?

2. What nationality is runner Gabriela Szabo?

3. Which rap band was formerly known as Spectrum City?

4. Who had a 1976 hit with the song *Dancing Queen*?

5. In which year was John F Kennedy elected US president?

6. In which African country is the city of Umtata?

7. Which singer/songwriter, born in Los Angeles, recorded the album *Little Criminals*?

8. Who wrote the 1882 play *An Enemy of the People*?

9. In which year was automatic timing first used in athletics at the Olympic Games?

10. 'Tomato sauce' is Australian rhyming slang for which animal?

Quiz 66

1 Who wrote the 1974 novel *Shardik*?

2 In which year was the first atomic bomb exploded?

3 In which century did US scientist Benjamin Franklin live?

4 To what is the term 'picture element' abbreviated in computer science?

5 Iapetus is a moon of which planet?

6 What is the name of the hill on which the city of Jerusalem stands?

7 In heraldry, what is the name given to the colour red?

8 What is the name of the wild mountain sheep of North Africa, also known as an aoudad?

9 In which Shakespeare play does the clown Launcelot Gobbo appear?

10 What type of creature is a coelacanth?

Quiz 67

1 In which African country is the city of Germiston, which houses the world's largest gold refinery?

2 In the Old Testament, which Hebrew patriarch built an ark?

3 Which comedy duo starred in the 1942 film *A-Haunting We Will Go*?

4 In which year was the Women's World Cup in cricket first held?

5 What nationality is golfer Marc Farry?

6 Which actor did Courteney Cox marry in 1999?

7 How many players has a beach volleyball team?

8 For what does the abbreviation ECG stand in medicine?

9 What was the nickname of US crime boss Charles Luciano?

10 Which Australian city is the state capital of Victoria?

Quiz 68

1 Who created the oriental villain Fu Manchu?

2 Which word was originally an abbreviation of the German word 'Fliegerabwehrkanone'?

3 In Greek mythology, who was the father of Icarus?

4 What sort of creature is an 'accentor'?

5 Which English king was killed at the Battle of Bosworth Field?

6 By what name was US comedian Louis Francis Cristillo better known?

7 Racing driver Dale Earnhardt was killed on the final lap of which famous race in 2001?

8 Which professional team golf event was first contested in 1927?

9 Which comic police force did Max Sennett create in his silent films?

10 Who was the Greek goddess of the moon?

Quiz 69

1 To which famous US comedian was Gracie Allen married?

2 Who said "Ask not what your country can do you for, ask what you can do for your country"?

3 What is the capital of Hungary?

4 Who did Telly Savalas play in the film *The Greatest Story Ever Told*?

5 What is the world's most common blood group?

6 Who wrote *A Clockwork Orange*?

7 Which Spanish surrealist artist painted *The Crucifixion* in 1951?

8 Which actress starred along with Lucy Liu and Drew Barrymore in the 2000 film remake of *Charlie's Angels*?

9 Which character was played by Michael Caine in *The Ipress File* and *Funeral in Berlin*?

10 The sackbut was a forerunner of which musical instrument?

Quiz 70

1 Which Canadian jazz pianist has 16 honorary degrees from North American universities?

2 Which African country was formerly called Upper Volta?

3 What is the title of the film sequel to *The Silence of the Lambs*?

4 What is the name of the country formerly known as Nyasaland?

5 Which US actress was known as The Sweater Girl in the 1940s?

6 Which US media mogul founded CNN?

7 Which German novelist wrote *Death in Venice* and *The Magic Mountain*?

8 Which actress starred with Bob Hope and Bing Crosby in the series of *Road to...* films?

9 Which Irish punk band's line-up on forming in 1975 was Bob Geldof on vocals, Johnnie Fingers on keyboards, Pete Briquette on bass and Gerry Cott and Garry Roberts on guitar?

10 Which actor played Starsky in the 1970s US cop series *Starsky and Hutch*?

Quiz 71

1 Who was known as 'the lady with the lamp'?

2 In the computer abbreviation ASCII, for what does the letter 'C' stand?

3 Of which US state is Lansing the capital?

4 Which of the British Isles has three legs on its flag?

5 What sort of creature is a 'piddock'?

6 Which Oscar-winning actor starred in the film *What Women Want*?

7 On which river does the city of Manchester stand?

8 What is the meaning of the title Fidei Defensor belonging to English monarchs?

9 Which US football team won Superbowl XLI?

10 Who wrote *The Day of the Triffids*?

Quiz 72

1 In which year was Nelson Mandela released from prison?

2 Which fictional bear is a friend of Christopher Robin?

3 In Greek mythology, which mountain nymph fell in love with Narcissus?

4 In Norse mythology, who was the god of mischief?

5 What creatures constitute the principal food of the aardwolf?

6 Which tennis player beat Serena and then Venus Williams in consecutive matches at the 2001 Australian Open?

7 Who was the first man to set foot on the moon?

8 In which European country is the city of Maastricht?

9 Which carbohydrate is also called milk sugar?

10 Which boxer was known as The Dark Destroyer?

Quiz 73

1 How many players make up an ice hockey team?

2 On which date is Hallowe'en celebrated?

3 In Christianity, what is the period from Ash Wednesday to Easter known as?

4 In which year did the artist Pablo Picasso die: 1987 or 1973?

5 In which novel by Thomas Hardy does the character Fanny Robin appear?

6 From which country was Dag Hammarskjold the second Secretary General of the United Nations?

7 At which Oxford college did Oscar Wilde study?

8 Who wrote the 2001 novel *Skipping Christmas*?

9 What is the common name of the plant *lonicera*?

10 Which writer lived in exile in France under the assumed name of Sebastian Melmoth?

Quiz 74

1 On which Italian bay does the volcano Vesuvius stand?

2 The attempted assassination of which pop artist and filmmaker was the subject of a 1996 film by Mary Harron?

3 Why is the bird named the hoopoe so called?

4 What in martial arts is one's choong sim?

5 Tbilisi is the capital city of which former Soviet republic?

6 Which member of the Eagles was lead guitarist in the group Barnstorm, who released the 1972 album *Barnstorm*?

7 Of what is paleozoology the scientific study?

8 Which painter's works include his 1948 *La Philosophie Dans le Boudoir*?

9 Who wrote the novel *The Odessa File*?

10 Which Canadian actor provided the voice of the orphaned mouse Stuart Little in the 2000 film of the same name?

Quiz 75

1 What was the name of Prince's character in the 1984 film *Purple Rain*?

2 In which ocean are the Marshall Islands?

3 Which US city was the setting for Ross and Rachel's drunken marriage in the sitcom *Friends*?

4 Which sculptor's works include the 1921 bronze *Turning Torso*?

5 If you suffer from 'balletomania', for what do you have a passion?

6 Which US prison is nicknamed Big Q?

7 What is a 'cockatoo' to an Australian criminal?

8 Which river flows through the Austrian capital, Vienna?

9 In which US state was the TV drama *The Waltons* set?

10 Who was the Czech composer of the opera *The Bartered Bride*?

Quiz 76

1 Who was the second son of Noah in the Old Testament?

2 Who composed the opera *La Bohème*?

3 Which 1977 World War II film concerned the failed Allied landings at Arnhem in Holland?

4 Who was the Dutch painter of *The Garden of Earthly Delights*?

5 What nationality is golfer Rikka Hakkarainen?

6 Which BNL hockey side signed Canadian Chad MacLeod in 1999?

7 The former penal colony of Devil's Island belongs to which island group?

8 The suburb of Laval is part of which major Canadian city?

9 Which island joined with Tanganyika to form Tanzania?

10 Georgian Bay is the north-east part of which North American Great Lake?

Quiz 77

1 What was the strange crime of German computer technician Armin Meiwes, who was brought to trial in 2003?

2 Which organization was replaced by the United Nations in 1945?

3 Which organization was initially formed by Iran, Iraq, Kuwait, Saudi Arabia and Venezuela in 1960?

4 Which planet comes first in Gustav Holst's *The Planets Suite?*

5 Following the end of World War II, until which year did the US occupy Japan?

6 What is the main religion of Japan?

7 In what respect is the Lost Sea in the US state of Tennessee the world's largest lake?

8 Cochin, Welsummer and Light Sussex are all breeds of which animal?

9 Which capital city, a one-time Olympics venue, stands at over 2,500 metres above sea level and has a museum dedicated to Leon Trotsky?

10 Which city started out as Gastown and is now the largest city in British Columbia?

Quiz 78

1 What does the computer programming language BASIC stand for?

2 Zeeland, Fyn, Lolland, Falster and Bornholm are the principals islands of which country?

3 Which country is the most popular destination for foreign tourists?

4 Which French oceanographer commanded the research vessel *Calypso*?

5 Which city is the capital of the Tuscany region of Italy?

6 Immortalized by the rhyme, the bridge of Avignon in France crosses which river?

7 Which baseball player featured in the lyrics of Simon and Garfunkel's *Mrs Robinson*?

8 The Flathead Lake Monster is said to exist in which US state?

9 Who wrote *Arms and the Man* and *Man and Superman*?

10 Into which superhero did Jim McGuire of the *Daily World Newspaper* turn after falling into a tankful of chemicals?

ANSWERS:
1 Beginners' All-Purpose Symbolic Instruction Code, 2 Denmark, 3 France, 4 Jacques Cousteau, 5 Florence, 6 Rhône, 7 Joe DiMaggio, 8 Montana, 9 George Bernard Shaw, 10 The Phantom.

Quiz 79

1 Which US city is served by George Bush Intercontinental Airport?

2 Reubens, Caravaggio and Bernini were all active during which art period?

3 Which 20th century Dutch artist and engraver is most famous for his interlocking shapes and manipulations of perspective, with works including *Day and Night* and *Waterfall*?

4 In 1942, which village in Czechoslovakia was ordered by Hitler to be destroyed and erased from the map as a reprisal for the assassination of Reinhard Heydrich?

5 Which Russian composer and professor of chemistry composed three symphonies and the symphonic poem *In the Steppes of Central Asia*?

6 Complete the phrase: "He that can does, he that cannot…"

7 The Prado Museum and Gallery is in which European capital city?

8 What was the nickname of the German fixed undercarriage dive-bomber of World War II?

9 Which is the world's best-selling commercial airliner?

10 Who was the first US president to be assassinated?

ANSWERS:
1 Houston, 2 Baroque, 3 M C Escher, 4 Lidice, 5 Borodin, 6 Teaches, 7 Madrid, 8 Stuka, 9 Boeing 737, 10 Abraham Lincoln.

Quiz 80

1 Which previously unknown Canadian songstress set the world on fire with the album *Jagged Little Pill*?

2 For which country was Linetta Wilson a 1996 Olympic swimming champion?

3 Which song by the Rolling Stones did Tori Amos cover in the 1992 EP *Crucify*?

4 In which year did Iraq invade Kuwait, leading to the first Gulf War?

5 The adjective 'gnathic' refers to which part of the body?

6 Which word in ballet is used to describe the tip of the toe?

7 In Canada, what is 'muskeg'?

8 What shape is the type of tomb known as a 'tholos'?

9 Where did John Lennon and Yoko Ono marry in 1969?

10 What is the name of the famous onion-domed, brightly painted Moscow cathedral?

Quiz 81

1 The 1956 film *Reach for the Sky* is based on whose life story?

2 Who voiced Stinky Pete in the film *Toy Story 2*?

3 How many times did Bobby Jones win the US Amateur Championship in golf?

4 In which sport is the Conn Smythe Trophy awarded?

5 Which female singer recorded the 2001 album *Read My Lips*?

6 Which singer recorded the 2000 album *Holy Wood (In the Shadow of the Valley of Death)*?

7 Which was the first element to be created artificially?

8 In which European capital city is the Institut Pasteur based?

9 Which condition does the acronym AIDS stand for?

10 In computing, what does ISDN stand for?

Quiz 82

1 In which European city are the Pushkin Museum of Fine Arts and the Kremlin?

2 In computing what does PCMCIA stand for?

3 In which century did British biologist Thomas Henry Huxley live?

4 Which boy band recorded the 2001 single *Pop*?

5 What unit of distance used in astronomy is equal to 0.3066 of a parsec?

6 Which 1979 record album by Michael Jackson spent over 170 weeks in the UK album chart?

7 The St John River, which forms part of the international boundary between the US and Canada, rises in which state?

8 Which Canada-born revue singer's films included 1967's *Thoroughly Modern Millie*?

9 Who was the wife of Cronus and mother of Zeus in Greek mythology?

10 What was the nickname of King Richard I of England?

Quiz 83

1 Which is the inner and longer of the two bones of the human forearm?

2 Which Argentinian was 1998 WBA Flyweight Boxing Champion?

3 Who plays the title rôle in the 2000 film *The Grinch*?

4 What nationality is golfer Wayne Riley?

5 What relationship was Mike Love to Brian, Carl and Dennis Wilson of The Beach Boys?

6 Which Japanese city hosted the 1998 Winter Olympic Games?

7 Who was the first man to win both the 200- and 400-metre gold medals at the same Olympic Games?

8 In Greek mythology, which race of creatures was part-horse and part-man?

9 What sort of blood cells are also known as leucocytes?

10 Which US folk singer wrote *Where Have All the Flowers Gone* and *Kisses Sweeter Than Wine*?

Quiz 84

1 Which British novelist wrote the bestseller *Room at the Top*?

2 From which English lake was Donald Campbell's *Bluebird* raised in 2001?

3 Which metal is added to copper to make brass?

4 Edward Whymper led the first team to climb which famous Swiss peak?

5 What is the capital of Canada's Yukon territory?

6 What was the former name of the German city of Chemnitz?

7 In which film does Marty go back to the year 1885?

8 What is the name of Viola's twin brother in Shakespeare's *Twelfth Night*?

9 Which pop star visited Britain in 2001 to address the Oxford Union on the subject of child welfare?

10 Which king did caricaturist James Gillray portray as Farmer George?

Quiz 85

1 Which Jane Austen novel begins: "It is a truth universally acknowledged that a single man in possession of a good fortune must be in want of a wife"?

2 What was the occupation of the character played by Jack Lemmon in the film *How to Murder Your Wife*?

3 In which country is the city of Faisalabad?

4 Which famous nanny was created by P L Travers?

5 What name is given to the winter dormancy of certain mammals?

6 What was the first name of the Scottish pirate Captain Kidd?

7 Which British tenor sang in the first performances of all Benjamin Britten's operas?

8 Do male or female sea horses carry the eggs until they hatch?

9 What is the surname of Emma in the novel by Jane Austen?

10 Which famous artist was the subject of the song by Don McLean which begins "Starry, starry night"?

Quiz 86

1 How many dogs take part in a greyhound race in Britain?

2 Naim Suleymanoglu from Turkey is a top name in which sport?

3 Which number lies between seven and eight on a dartboard?

4 Battledore is an ancient forerunner of which modern racquet game?

5 Which US director made the films *Carrie*, *Scarface* and *The Untouchables*?

6 Against which disease can the BCG vaccination offer protection?

7 What is added to vodka to make a Boody Mary cocktail?

8 In which athletics event did Bob Beamon hold the world record for 23 years?

9 Which female French singer is best known for the song *Non, Je Ne Regrette Rien*?

10 In the Old Testament, which beast is said to have 'limbs like bars of iron'?

Quiz 87

1 Which Canadian jazz diva married English musician Elvis Costello in 2003?

2 Which Apollo space mission was manned by Charles Conrad, Alan Bean and Richard Gordon?

3 The film *Picnic at Hanging Rock* begins on which day, normally associated with love?

4 What word comes from the Persian for a public market district of a town?

5 Which comet is shown on the Bayeux Tapestry?

6 What name is given to a musical composition for six instruments?

7 Which Spanish painter was noted for his Blue Period in the early 20th century?

8 Which actor played eight rôles in the 2000 film sequel *Nutty Professor II: the Klumps*?

9 Which US actress was the elder sister of Joan Fontaine?

10 What nickname was given to the M9A1 shoulder-held rocket launcher of World War II?

Quiz 88

1 Which is the highest-pitched woodwind instrument in an orchestra?

2 Who was the first professional England cricketer to be knighted?

3 What is the capital of Greece?

4 In which novel by Charles Dickens does the character Bill Sykes appear?

5 In the Old Testament, which Midianite priest became Moses' father-in-law?

6 Which US actress became Princess Grace of Monaco?

7 With which athletics event is Sergey Bubka associated?

8 Which US writer claimed that "men seldom make passes at girls who wear glasses"?

9 What is the oldest of the three classic races that constitute the American Triple Crown?

10 In Greek mythology, what name was given to a one-eyed giant?

Quiz 89

1 In what type of car did Michael J Fox travel through time in the *Back to the Future* films?

2 Which star of the US sitcom *Roseanne* appeared in the 2000 film *Coyote Ugly*?

3 What were the first names of the Harts in the US drama series *Hart to Hart*?

4 With which musical instrument is Coleman Hawkins associated?

5 In Chinese philosophy, what name is given to the ethereal substance of which everything is composed?

6 Which literary family is associated with Haworth Parsonage in West Yorkshire?

7 Which clarinettist had a hit with *Stranger on the Shore* in 1961?

8 What was the name of the city where TV's *The Jetsons* lived?

9 In Greek mythology, who killed the Minotaur?

10 What is added to vodka to make a Screwdriver cocktail?

Quiz 90

1 Which poison is represented by the letters Cn?

2 Which film was advertised as having a cast of 125,000?

3 What was the surname of the uncle and nephew who discovered the north magnetic pole?

4 Which English poet wrote *The Rime of the Ancient Mariner*?

5 Which English fashion designer opened the boutique *Bazaar* in the Kings Road in 1957?

6 Which actress starred as Buffy the Vampire Slayer in the TV series of the same name?

7 Who wrote the novel *All Quiet on the Western Front*?

8 In which city is the former cathedral of Hagia Sophia?

9 What is the name of Patrick Stewart's character in *Star Trek: The Next Generation*?

10 What is the SI derived unit of radiation dose equivalent?

Quiz 91

1 Who wrote *The Wonderful Wizard of Oz*?

2 Which famous volcano between Java and Sumatra erupted catastrophically in 1883?

3 Which Australian tree is also called a gum tree?

4 What name is given to the study of human improvements by genetic means?

5 Which Mongul emperor was the grandson of Genghis Khan?

6 What was Miss Piggy's surname in the TV show *The Muppets*?

7 What is the sequel to the film *101 Dalmatians*?

8 Which US president was known as Old Hickory?

9 With which branch of mathematics is Euclid chiefly associated?

10 What was the Greek name for Khufu, builder of the Great Pyramid at Giza?

Quiz 92

1 Which Danish-born comedian and pianist died in 2000 at the age of 91?

2 Who wrote the influential book *How to Win Friends and Influence People*?

3 In which US state is the headland known as Diamond Head?

4 Which famous square is on the east side of the Kremlin in Moscow?

5 What nationality was the composer Carl Nielsen?

6 What was the first name of the famous furniture designer Heppelwhite?

7 Which British boxer needed emergency surgery after a fight in December 2000?

8 What name is given to a monologue in which a character in a play speaks his thoughts aloud?

9 Which sociologist, historian and economist co-wrote the Communist Manifesto with Friedrich Engels?

10 What name is given to an aquatic mammal with four limbs modified into flippers?

Quiz 93

1 What nationality was the composer Paul Hindemith?

2 Which fictional character made his first appearance in the novel *The Little White Bird*?

3 Who designed the wedding dress worn by Catherine Zeta Jones when she married Michael Douglas?

4 What sort of plant is a 'lady's slipper'?

5 What form of exercise was popularised by Bill Bowerman in a 1967 book?

6 In which South American country did Prince William spend ten weeks as part of an Operation Raleigh expedition?

7 What sort of dog has Labrador and golden varieties?

8 Which great Czech distance runner died in 2000 at the age of 78?

9 Which British actress starred in *The Killing of Sister George* and *Entertaining Mr Sloane*?

10 What is the name of the fielding position in cricket between cover and mid-off?

Quiz 94

1 What monetary unit of Israel is worth one hundredth of a shekel?

2 In the high jump, what name is given to the manoeuvre of jumping over the horizontal bar backwards and head first?

3 What is the capital of Costa Rica?

4 What is the name given to the set of chalk stacks off the west coast of the Isle of Wight?

5 What is the chief port of Tanzania?

6 Which pop group's record albums include *Black Celebration* and *Construction Time Again*?

7 Who was the male star of the 1989 film *How to Get Ahead in Advertising*, directed by Bruce Robinson?

8 What is the capital of the US state of Delaware?

9 What name is given to the indicator of stock market prices; based on the share values of 30 blue-chip stocks listed on the New York Stock Exchange?

10 Which city in south-eastern Germany on the Elbe River was almost totally destroyed by British and US air raids in 1945?

Quiz 95

1 Which girl group had a 1966 hit with the song *Sweet Talking Guy*?

2 Which actor directed and starred in the 1973 film *Antony and Cleopatra*?

3 Who was the first husband of actress Brigitte Bardot?

4 In 1989, Burma changed its name to what?

5 What did the Netherlands East Indies become in 1945?

6 In which month is the horserace Le Prix de l'Arc de Triomph run?

7 Which island in Indonesia is the largest of the Lesser Sunda Islands?

8 In Hindu mythology, what is the food of the gods that bestows immortality?

9 What are the names of the rival gangs in the 1961 film *West Side Story*?

10 Which rock star produced the 2001 film *Enigma*?

Quiz 96

1 Which Toronto-based rock power trio have been on top of the stadium rock world since 1978?

2 At which Olympic sport have Louis Debray and Yevgeny Petrov been champions?

3 The word 'honcho' meaning boss, derives from which language?

4 In which game might you employ a zwischenzug?

5 What does the phrase 'foie gras' mean, as in 'pâté de foie gras'?

6 For which sporting activity would you wear salopettes?

7 The branch of science known as odontology refers to which part of the human body?

8 Which 1876 novel by Mark Twain features the character Becky Thatcher?

9 Which European capital city is the setting for the 1988 film *American Roulette*?

10 Which Rolling Stones song did Eddie and the Hotrods cover on their *Live at the Marquee* EP?

Quiz 97

1 Os is the symbol for which chemical element?

2 Which Nobel prize-winning physicist was born in Tonbridge, Kent, in 1903?

3 Which has the higher melting point: copper or iron?

4 What is the name of the Polish river on which the city of Poznan stands?

5 Which famous English ballerina was born Lilian Alicia Marks?

6 Which actor plays a sleazy tabloid publisher in the 1997 film *LA Confidential*?

7 Who plays Roz Doyle in the sitcom *Frasier*?

8 With which card-game is Ely Culbertson associated?

9 *Little Girl Lost* is a biography of which Hollywood actress?

10 Which singer has been given exclusive use of the island of Ellidaey by the Icelandic government?

Quiz 98

1 Which actor appeared in TV's *Ally McBeal* as attorney Larry Paul, after serving time in prison?

2 In which country was landscape painter John La Farge born in 1835?

3 How was actress Grace Kelly killed?

4 What is the meaning of the word 'karate'?

5 Who did Muhammad Ali beat in 1975 to retain his World Heavyweight crown?

6 In which game might you use a 'bonce'?

7 St Boniface is a suburb of which Canadian city?

8 What is a 'bullace': is it a type of bird or is it a tree?

9 Of what quantity is the ampere the SI unit?

10 In which Asian country is the city of Suwon?

Quiz 99

1 The watercolours of which painter and poet include *Job Confessing his Presumption God, Who Answers from the Whirlwind*?

2 Which European country administers the Canary Islands?

3 Which member of The Beach Boys recorded the 1977 solo album *Going Public*?

4 What are you in New Zealand if you are 'boohai'?

5 Which pioneering singer-songwriter was backed by The Crickets?

6 What is the name of Dick Dastardly's canine companion in the cartoon series *Wacky Races*?

7 With which instrument was the jazz musician Buddy Rich associated?

8 Of what is 'otorhinolaryngology' the scientific study?

9 Which is further east: Cannes or Nice?

10 Why might you avoid a 'euripus' if you were a sailor?

Quiz 100

1 Which Canadian novel written by Michael Ondaatje won the Man Booker prize in 1992 and was adapted into an Academy Award winning film?

2 What type of creature might have a 'banged' tail?

3 What would you do with 'entremets'?

4 In which European country is the Furka Pass?

5 Which guitarist recorded the album *Money and Cigarettes*?

6 What is the meaning of the Latin phrase 'ut supra'?

7 On which Hawaiian island is Pearl Harbor?

8 Who wrote the 1819 novel *The Bride of Lammermoor*?

9 What is the cube root of the number one?

10 Which sex symbol actress of the 1950s and 1960s was born Vera Jayne Palmer in 1933?

Quiz 101

1 By what name was jazz composer and pianist Ferdinand Joseph La Menthe better known?

2 What is the name of the alphabet used for writing Russian?

3 What were the names of The Blues Brothers played by John Belushi and Dan Ackroyd in the 1908 film?

4 Which was the first film of the *National Lampoon's* series to star Chevy Chase?

5 Who played the lead in the film *Life of Brian*?

6 Which British dramatist wrote *The Caretaker* and *The Birthday Party*?

7 Which is the brightest star in the constellation Leo?

8 Which holiday is observed on the first Monday in September in the US?

9 What is the executive capital and largest city of Tanzania?

10 Which hand tool was used for threshing grain until the mid-19th century?

Quiz 102

1 What sort of puzzle originated as education devices to teach geography?

2 Who was the head of RAF Fighter Command during the Battle of Britain?

3 Which *Fatal Attraction* actress starred in the 1991 film *Meeting Venus* as a lead soprano in the fictional *Opera Europa*?

4 What was the name of the lion in *The Chronicles of Narnia*?

5 Kurt Cobain was the lead singer with which grunge rock group?

6 Which oriental eating utensils originated in China?

7 Which Russian city was formerly called Petrograd?

8 Who wrote the 1976 science fiction novel *Children of Dune*?

9 Which type of writing paper measuring 13½ inches by 17 inches is named after the watermark which was formerly used on it?

10 Which opera by Amilcare Ponchielli contains the ballet *Dance of the Hours*?

Quiz 103

1 Which comic book character's alter ego is Dr Banner?

2 What was the middle name of showman Phineas T Barnum?

3 Who directed the 2000 film *Erin Brockovich*?

4 What is the real name of Guns N' Roses guitarist Izzy Stradlin?

5 Who was the original female singer in the group The Beautiful South?

6 'Tom Thumb' is Australian rhyming slang for which alcoholic drink?

7 What type of creature is a galah: a cockatoo or a kangaroo?

8 Which England Test cricket captain was known as The Champion?

9 In which year did electronic digital computer Colossus first become operational?

10 Of what is seismology the study?

Quiz 104

1 What nationality is the cyclist Eddy Merckx?

2 With which instrument was Yehudi Menuhin associated?

3 Which US city is nicknamed Bean Town?

4 In which European country is the ski resort of Serre-Chevalier?

5 What was Michael Caine's character's name in the 1967 film *Billion Dollar Brain*?

6 Which actor's son plays the kidnapped child in the 1996 film *Ransom*?

7 At which sport were Irina Karavaeva and Alexander Rusakov world champions in 2005?

8 In which sport was Denny Hume active during the 1970s?

9 Who set a world record of 26:38.08 for the 10,000 metres on 23 August 1996?

10 Who wrote the 2001 self-help-cum-autobiographical book *Take It From Me: Life's a Struggle But You Can Win*?

Quiz 105

1 In which country was the actor Robert Donat born?

2 With which sport was Geoff Capes most famously associated?

3 What was the name of Othello's wife in Shakespeare's play of the same name?

4 In the Old Testament, where was the birthplace of King David?

5 With which sport is Reggie Jackson associated?

6 What is Salman Rushdie's real first name?

7 For which month is emerald the traditional birthstone?

8 Which marine creature includes the varieties hermit, spider and king?

9 Which former country was also known as the GDR?

10 Which Texas city has an American football team called The Cowboys?

Quiz 106

1 How many countries changed their currencies to the Euro in January 2002?

2 Which Hungarian-born actress provided the voice of Bianca in the Disney *Rescuers* films?

3 In which English county is the Vale of Eden?

4 What was artist John Callcott Horsley the first to design?

5 What is a two-man bobsleigh called?

6 Which beauty contest was the brainchild of Eric Morley, who died in 2000?

7 In which German city would you see the Brandenburg Gate?

8 In computing, for what does HTML stand?

9 Which imaginary country was the setting for *The Prisoner of Zenda*?

10 Which state underwent several recounts to decide the outcome of the 2000 US presidential election?

Quiz 107

1 Which Bavarian town was the site of the first concentration camp set up by the Nazis?

2 Which US singer/songwriter wrote *Blowin' in the Wind*?

3 Which US author wrote *The Fall of the House of Usher*?

4 Which actor starred as a theatrical entrepreneur and serial-killer in the 1968 film *No Way to Treat a Lady*?

5 Which UK garage artist released the debut album *Born to Do It*?

6 Which form of recreation originated on paved areas along California beaches in the 1960s?

7 What is the name of the Barber of Seville in the play by Beaumarchais?

8 Which music-hall comedienne and singer was born Grace Stansfield?

9 What was the tallest building in the world before the completion of the Chrysler Building in New York in 1930?

10 Which French composer wrote *The Sorcerer's Apprentice*?

Quiz 108

1 What sort of creature is a prairie dog?

2 In which US state is Dodge City?

3 How many legs has a lobster?

4 In which country is the city of Eindhoven?

5 In which year were the Winter Olympics held in Grenoble, France?

6 What name is given to the fatty substance released by sebaceous glands?

7 Which star of the film *Billy Elliot* won the Best Actor award at the 2001 BAFTAs?

8 How many feet are there in one yard?

9 Which winter sport event combines cross-country skiing and rifle shooting?

10 Who was the first athlete to win two Olympic marathons?

Quiz 109

1 Name the Montreal-born author of *St Urbain's Horsemen* and *Barney's Version*.

2 Which Irish poet wrote *The Lake Isle of Innisfree*?

3 Which king led England into the Hundred Years War with France?

4 Who sculpted the statue of Peter Pan in London's Kensington Gardens?

5 Which English queen was the daughter of King Henry VIII and Anne Boleyn?

6 By what first name was Emad Mohamed al-Fayed known?

7 With which instrument is jazz musician Jack Teagarden associated?

8 Who made his directorial debut with *Star Trek III: The Search for Spock*?

9 By what name was World Heavyweight Boxing Champion Charles Liston better known?

10 Roald Dahl wrote the script for which Bond film?

Quiz 110

1 Which English poet wrote *A Shropshire Lad*?

2 From which two places did the Bren gun get its name?

3 What name is given to the natural painkillers secreted by the brain that resemble opiates?

4 Which US silent film star was known as The Man of a Thousand Faces?

5 Which nonsense poem by Lewis Carroll is subtitled *An Agony in Eight Fits*?

6 What name is given to the two dots placed above a vowel in German?

7 Which sign of the zodiac governs the period from 19 February to 20 March?

8 What sort of creature is a 'moccasin'?

9 Which child star sang *On the Good Ship Lollipop* in the 1934 film *Bright Eyes*?

10 On whose book was the film *Fahrenheit 451* based?

Quiz 111

1 Which narcotic was removed from Coca Cola's formula in 1905?

2 Which rock star's leather trousers were sold for £28,000 at Sotheby's in 1996?

3 Who starred as the athlete fighting for his free will in the 1975 film *Rollerball*?

4 What sort of animal was the star of the 1995 *Babe*?

5 In which country is a 'grosz' a monetary unit?

6 Which country in Africa is immediately west of Western Zambia?

7 In the US, what is a 'flack'?

8 Where was William Rufus killed by an arrow in 1100?

9 What is the English equivalent of a 'dome fastener'?

10 What was unusual about the three albums by Eva Cassidy which reached No 1 in the UK charts in 2001-2003?

Quiz 112

1 Which British Formula 1 racing driver survived a Learjet crash in May 2000?

2 Which city hosted the 1980 Olympic Games?

3 What is a 'jaconet': a type of fabric or a kind of soldier?

4 In which Australian state are the towns of Alice Springs and Darwin?

5 Which female singer had a hit single with the song *What a Girl Wants*?

6 How is the River Granta, which flows through the English city of Cambridge, otherwise known?

7 Which continent has the larger land mass: Antarctica or South America?

8 S A Waksman received a Nobel prize in medicine for his discovery of which antibiotic?

9 Of what is malocology the scientific study?

10 Which comic actor was married to Tuesday Weld and Suzy Kendall?

Quiz 113

1 What form of transport is a 'travois'?

2 What is another word for an alligator pear?

3 Which country in Africa is immediately west of Egypt?

4 In which game is a 'cayman' used?

5 Which US state is further north: Alabama or Utah?

6 Which Spanish artist's paintings included 1934's *Girl Reading at a Table*?

7 If an actor 'dries' what does he or she do?

8 In which industry would neroli oil be used?

9 What is the square root of 16?

10 Which legendary singer/songwriter was killed on 8 December 1980?

Quiz 114

1 Which 1995 Jean Becker film starred Gerard Depardieu and Vanessa Paradis?

2 In which decade did gangster Al Capone die?

3 In which year did Texas gain independence from Mexico?

4 What shape is a 'clevis'?

5 Rathlin Island lies between which two parts of the British Isles?

6 If you have 'hypermnesia' what are you good at?

7 The name of which god of the Philistines in the Old Testament meant 'lord of flies'?

8 What was the name given to the journey of about 6,000 miles undertaken by around 100,000 Chinese communists between 1934 and 1935?

9 Who was the author of the play *The Glass Menagerie*?

10 Who played Carolyn in the film *American Beauty*?

Quiz 115

1 What name is given to the back part of a golf club head where it bends to join the shaft?

2 Which cult TV series featured Kyle MacLachan as agent Dale Cooper?

3 What nationality is cricketer Usman Afzaal?

4 Under the pseudonym of Apollo C Vermouth, who produced *I'm the Urban Spaceman* by the Bonzo Dog Do-Dah Band?

5 On which island is the Canadian seaport of Sydney?

6 Who was the author of the classic novel *The Three Musketeers*?

7 Rothesay is a town on the east coast of which Scottish island?

8 Who wrote the 1947 play *A Streetcar Named Desire*?

9 How many moons has Mars?

10 Which French actress stars in the 1969 comedy film *The April Fools*, with Jack Lemmon?

Quiz 116

1 Name the Canadian author of *The Blind Assassin*, winner of the Man Booker prize in 2001.

2 Which Tammy Wynette song was covered by Lyle Lovett on the album *Lyle Lovett and his Large Band*?

3 Which US city is nicknamed Big D?

4 What sort of animal is a macaque?

5 What type of entertainer is an engastrimyth?

6 To which period of time did the word 'sennight' refer?

7 What item of clothing is also known as a 'filibeg'?

8 Name the place near Lewes in Sussex which was the site of a famous scientific forgery of 1912.

9 What was the name of the ranger in the cartoon series *Yogi Bear*?

10 What nationality is alpine skier Spela Pretnar?

Quiz 117

1 Which group's albums included the live recording *Bless Its Pointed Little Head*?

2 To what did the group The Detours change their name in 1964?

3 Which British album went straight to No 1 in the US charts in 2000?

4 In the hexadecimal system, what letter represents the number 15?

5 The largest of the seas of the Moon is the Mare Imbrium: what does this translate to?

6 Lake Iliamna is the largest lake in which US state?

7 In which sport did Inna Ryskal of the USSR win four Olympic medals from 1964 to 1976?

8 *Makes Me Wonder* was a Top Five hit for which group in 2007?

9 Whose album *Favourite Worst Nightmare* was a hit in 2007?

10 What is the real name of the comedienne Ruby Wax?

ANSWERS:
1 Jefferson Airplane, 2 The Who, 3 Kid A by Radiohead, 4 F, 5 Sea of Rains, 6 Alaska, 7 Volleyball, 8 Maroon 5, 9 Arctic Monkeys, 10 Ruby Wachs.

120

Quiz 118

1 In which European country is the city of Katowice?

2 In which novel by Tolstoy does Konstantin Levin appear?

3 What was the title of actor David Niven's first autobiography?

4 Who is the hero of John Buchan's novel *The Thirty-Nine Steps*?

5 Which code used in telegraphy consists of dots and dashes?

6 In which 1999 Woody Allen film did Sean Penn play fictitious 1930s jazz guitarist Emmet Ray?

7 Which 1967 film set in America's deep south starred Sidney Poitier and Rod Steiger?

8 Which group recorded the hit album *Minutes To Midnight*?

9 Which US guitarist and composer was the leader of the Mothers of Invention?

10 What name is given to a verbal device for aiding the memory, such as "i before e except after c"?

Quiz 119

1   Which billionaire stood as a candidate in the US presidential elections in 1992 and 1996?

2   What sort of creature is a 'mud puppy'?

3   Who did Pat Cash beat in the Men's Final of Wimbledon in 1987?

4   What name is given to the outermost region of the Sun's atmosphere?

5   Which character in Greek mythology fell in love with his own reflection?

6   Who wrote *On the Origin of Species by Means of Natural Selection*?

7   Which prolific US author wrote *Riders of the Purple Sage*?

8   Which is the sixth book of the Old Testament?

9   Which US lawman killed Billy the Kid?

10 Which young Jewish girl is famous for the diary she kept while her family hid from the Nazis in Amsterdam?

Quiz 120

1 Which Russian leader was first associated with the policies of Glasnost and Perestroika?

2 Which former American football star was acquitted of murder in October 1995?

3 What name is given to the tiles used in a mosaic?

4 Which country hosted the Football World Cup in 1990?

5 What is the name given to the common foot infection caused by a fungus?

6 Which former British coin was worth a quarter of an old (pre-decimal) penny?

7 From which track event was Ben Johnson disqualified after winning at the 1998 Olympics?

8 In which year did Salt Lake City, USA, hold the Winter Olympics?

9 Which English seaside resort became a city in the year 2000?

10 Which Welsh artist painted portraits of George Bernard Shaw, Dylan Thomas and James Joyce?

Quiz 121

1 In which Canadian province is Algonquin Provincial Park?

2 Which English artist is best known for *A Rake's Progress*?

3 What is the northernmost point of the British Isles?

4 Which former silent film star is best known for her portrayal of Norma Desmond in the 1950 film *Sunset Boulevard*?

5 How many squares has a chessboard?

6 Which feature of chronic alcoholism is known as the DTs?

7 Which horror film actor was born William Henry Pratt?

8 Who directed the films *To Have and Have Not*, *The Big Sleep* and *Rio Bravo*?

9 What colour is the ball worth three points in snooker?

10 For which soccer club did Ronaldo leave Barcelona?

Quiz 122

1 Of which country did Jean-Bédel Bokassa proclaim himself emperor in 1977?

2 How many players are there in a Gaelic football team?

3 What name is given to the Japanese art of flower arranging?

4 A daguerreotype is an early form of what?

5 Which product did soap salesman William Wrigley Jr begin distributing in 1892?

6 Who is the patron saint of music?

7 In which European country is the summer and ski resort of Zell am See?

8 Who wrote *Rebecca of Sunnybrook Farm*?

9 What was the first name of the composer Mussorgsky?

10 The Kara Sea is an arm of which ocean?

Quiz 123

1 What is the title of the Clement Moore poem which begins "'Twas the night before Christmas…"?

2 Which actor appeared in *Apocalypse Now* and *Superman*?

3 Who is generally regarded as the first British prime minister?

4 What number wood in golf was formerly known as a 'spoon'?

5 What name is given to the deliberate and systematic destruction of a racial, religious or ethnic group?

6 Which US actor starred in *Twelve Angry Men* and *On Golden Pond*?

7 Who composed the symphony No 6 commonly known as *The Pastoral*?

8 Which three sports are included in the triathlon?

9 Which branch of mathematics takes its name from the Greek for 'earth measurement'?

10 Which horse won the British Grand National in 1973, 1974 and 1977?

Quiz 124

1 In which sport is the term 'hookcheck' often used?

2 Cardinal Richelieu was the chief minister of which French monarch?

3 What sort of creatures transmit Lyme disease?

4 What nationality is swimmer Pieter van den Hoogenband?

5 In which city is the US governing body of basketball, the NBA, based?

6 Who wrote the stage play *Cat on a Hot Tin Roof*?

7 What name is given to the strap which runs between the reins and the girth of a horse and prevents it from carrying its head too high?

8 Which river flows through the Sea of Galilee?

9 Gatun Lake is part of which canal?

10 In which ocean are the volcanic D'Entrecasteaux Islands?

Quiz 125

1 In which country is Mount Sir Sandford in the Selkirk Mountains?

2 Who were the two male leads in the 1997 film *Blood and Wine*?

3 Who was the designer of the British aircraft the Spitfire, which was used in the Battle of Britain?

4 Who is the female star of the 2000 film *The Next Best Thing*?

5 Which Oscar-winning actress played Pearl Slaghoople in the 1994 film *The Flintstones*?

6 Who played Mr Step in the 1997 film *Spice World*?

7 Who won the 1998 World Championship snooker title?

8 In fencing, what is a 'balestra'?

9 What type of creature is a jumping mouse: a bird or a rodent?

10 What is the name given to the end of a hammer head opposite to the striking face?

Quiz 126

1 If you suffer from apnoea, what are you unable to do?

2 The Italian dessert 'tiramisu' derives its name from which phrase?

3 In horticulture, what does the word 'ananthous' mean?

4 Which Phrygian goddess of nature was often called 'the mother of the gods'?

5 What nationality is cyclist Paolo Bettini?

6 In aeronautics, which organization is represented by the initials ESA?

7 In which year did John Logie Baird first transmit pictures between London and Glasgow using telephone lines?

8 The large moon Miranda is a satellite of which planet of the solar system?

9 Symbolic, connectionist and evolutionary are the three types of what?

10 Which US stand-up comedian and film actor appeared as a conman in the 1997 film *The Spanish Prisoner*?

Quiz 127

1 Who is the female star of the 2000 film *Stigmata*?

2 Which group had a 1985 hit with *Sex Over the Phone*?

3 For what was Chuck Berry imprisoned in 1979?

4 René Goscinny and Albert Uderzo were the creators of which famous French cartoon character hero?

5 What was the surname of the three brothers who were in the original line-up of The Beach Boys?

6 Which *Four Weddings and a Funeral* actress starred in the 1995 film *Unstrung Heroes*?

7 Which arch-villain was played by John Shea in the TV series *The New Adventures of Superman*?

8 Holly Golightly was Audrey Hepburn's character in which film of 1961?

9 Who had a UK No 1 hit in 1972 with *You Wear It Well*?

10 Which controversial former American football star played Nordberg in the *Naked Gun* films?

Quiz 128

1 In which Far Eastern country is the port city of Pusan?

2 Which European city is further north: Moscow or Newcastle?

3 Which science fiction writer wrote the 1905 novel *A Modern Utopia*?

4 What was the subject of Edward Bulwer-Lytton's disaster novel of 1834 concerning events in 79AD?

5 What nationality is the 1991 Wimbledon tennis champion Michael Stich?

6 Which black US athlete upset Adolf Hitler at the 1936 Berlin Olympics by winning four gold medals?

7 How many balls are used in a game of snooker?

8 Pickles the dog enjoyed worldwide fame in 1966 after he found which sports trophy?

9 Where would you find a structure called an 'empennage': on a ship or on an aircraft?

10 In which European country is the ski resort of Cervinia?

Quiz 129

1 If you are performing 'oscitancy', what are you doing?

2 What was the title of Kylie Minogue's first UK No 1 single?

3 Which veteran rock group released an album in 1966 entitled *Don't Stop*?

4 Which Canadian group recorded the 2000 album *Maroon*?

5 Approximately how many islands constitute the Cyclades group in the Aegean Sea: is it 220, 320 or 420?

6 In US politics, who carries the nickname 'the Veep'?

7 In which European country is the town of Gouda?

8 What is an 'elf-cup'?

9 Which English monarch was crowned in 1558?

10 What is a 'caparison'?

Quiz 130

1 Which famous English landscape artist's works include *The Vale of Dedham*?

2 In which year was Anne Boleyn executed?

3 Which body of water in Scotland does the Kincardine Bridge span?

4 Who recorded the 2001 album *Hot Shot*?

5 In which African country is the resort of Sharm El Sheikh?

6 Which star of the *X Files* TV series played Lily Bart in the film *The House of Mirth*?

7 Which modern US fighter aircraft is also called The Fighting Falcon?

8 What name is given to the fruits of plants of the genus *Ficus*?

9 What is the state capital of Utah?

10 In which year was the Channel Tunnel officially opened?

Quiz 131

1 Which prominent newspaper tycoon renounced his Canadian citizenship in 2001 in order to be appointed to Britain's House of Lords?

2 How many yards are there in one furlong?

3 What was the pen-name of Charles Lutwidge Dodgson?

4 In which country are the Plains of Abraham?

5 Which weather phenomenon takes its name from the Spanish for 'the child'?

6 Who wrote the children's story *James and the Giant Peach*?

7 Which country is known as Suomi in its native language?

8 In which year did the reggae artist Bob Marley die?

9 Which Hollywood heart-throb was the guitarist of the rock group P?

10 Which 1970 Ken Loach film starred David Bradley as a boy who becomes obsessed with a bird of prey?

Quiz 132

1 Which singer/songwriter won an Oscar for his score for the 1971 film *Shaft*?

2 Which US union leader mysteriously disappeared in 1975?

3 Which controversial British artist is best known for works such as *Mother and Child Divided*?

4 Which is the highest navigable lake in the world?

5 Albuquerque is the largest city of which US state?

6 Of which country is New Britain a part?

7 Which Latin legal term means 'you should have the body'?

8 Which sport involves 'the snatch', 'the clean' and 'the jerk'?

9 What name is given to radioactive material which settles on the Earth's surface following a nuclear explosion?

10 Who wrote the horror novel *Dracula*?

Quiz 133

1 Staten Island is a borough of which US city?

2 Which member of Whistler's family features in his most famous painting?

3 In which year did beach volleyball become an Olympic sport?

4 What were the surnames of the animators who created *Tom and Jerry*, *The Flintstones* and *Scooby Doo*?

5 In which country is the city of Abadan?

6 Which jazz pianist and composer won an Oscar for his score for the film *Round Midnight*?

7 What was Mickey Mouse's original name?

8 What does AC stand for in physics?

9 Which English romantic poet wrote *Tintern Abbey* and *The Prelude*?

10 What is the capital of the former Soviet state of Azerbaijan?

Quiz 134

1 Of which Central African country was Milton Obote the president from 1966 to 1971 and from 1980 to 1985?

2 Which German author wrote the short novel *Death in Venice*?

3 What was the official newspaper of the Communist Party in the old Soviet Union?

4 What name was given to the bubonic plague epidemic which ravaged Europe in the 14th century?

5 Which famous actor played Bill Sykes in the 1968 film version of *Oliver!*?

6 Which director made a cameo appearance in every one of his films from *The Lodger* of 1926 onwards?

7 Which 1990 film starred Al Pacino as a cop in pursuit of a criminal played by Robert De Niro?

8 Which country takes its name from the Latin word for 'southern'?

9 What is the general name for any hoofed mammal?

10 Which Roman highway running across Italy was named after Appius Claudius Caecus?

Quiz 135

1 Which form of partly-dehydrated gypsum is used for making casts and moulds?

2 Of which country is the shekel the basic monetary unit?

3 Which Canadian city is the capital of Ontario?

4 Which Canadian novelist wrote *The Apprenticeship of Duddy Kravitz*?

5 What does the 'G' stand for in the name of the film company MGM?

6 Which waterway linking the Pacific and Atlantic Oceans was completed in 1914?

7 What name is given to a score of one over par for a hole in golf?

8 What name is given to a space devoid of matter?

9 Which British author wrote *Three Men in a Boat*?

10 Which singer was born Annie Mae Bullock in 1939?

Quiz 136

1 Which critically acclaimed Canadian author wrote *The Stone Diaries*?

2 Who was the youngest man to have won all four of golf's major championships?

3 Which Roman historian wrote a history of Rome in 142 volumes?

4 What name is given to members of the United Society of Believers in Christ's Second Appearing?

5 Which former defence secretary did George W Bush choose as his running mate?

6 In computing, what does GUI stand for?

7 Which is the second largest mountain system in North America?

8 What was the popular name for the gallows which stood close to the present-day site of Marble Arch in London?

9 Which former star of *ER* appeared in the film *The Perfect Storm*?

10 In Longfellow's famous poem, who does Hiawatha marry?

Quiz 137

1 Who was the first actress to receive two Oscars before the age of 30?

2 Which Belgian city was the site of the first battle between British and German forces in World War I?

3 Which large triangular muscle covering the shoulder serves to raise the arm laterally?

4 What was the pen-name of Samuel Langhorne Clemens?

5 Which hoisting device used on ships is named after a 17th century English hangman?

6 Who was the fifth wife of King Henry VIII of England?

7 Which actress starred opposite Harrison Ford in the film thriller *What Lies Beneath*?

8 Which actor's childhood nickname was Tootsie?

9 Which boy band became the first act to have seven UK No 1 singles in a row?

10 What name is given to 15 July, which is supposed to set the weather for 40 days thereafter?

Quiz 138

1 Which French fashion designer launched the first 'ready-to-wear' collection for men, in 1960?

2 Who was the first black officer to hold the highest military post in the USA?

3 Which novel by Jeffrey Archer describes the competition between four men to become prime minister?

4 The powerful defoliant sprayed by US forces in Vietnam was known by what name?

5 Which animal is also called a honey-badger?

6 Which pop star bought a piano which belonged to John Lennon for more than £1 million at auction in 2000?

7 Who was the Greek goddess of agriculture?

8 Which food additive is also known as MSG?

9 What kind of animal was Flipper in the 1960s TV series of that name?

10 Which US author wrote *The Catcher in the Rye*?

Quiz 139

1 At which film festival are the Golden Lions awarded?

2 Which ship, launched in 1906, became the basis of battleship design for more than 50 years?

3 Who wrote the music for the ballet *Coppélia*?

4 Who was the first gymnast to score a perfect 10 in Olympic competition?

5 Which actor made his final film appearance as Proximo in *Gladiator*?

6 From which country does the wine Tokay come?

7 Which South African Zulu organization was founded by Chief Buthelezi in 1975?

8 Which colourless acid found in sour milk is used in the preservative E270?

9 What is the common name of the poisonous plant *hyoscyamus niger* which yields the drug hyoscyamine?

10 Who wrote the 1937 novel *The Citadel?*

Quiz 140

1 How many players are in a polo team?

2 Whose stories include *The Legend of Sleepy Hollow*?

3 Who sang the title song for the 1965 film *What's New Pussycat*?

4 Who wrote the 1937 book *Of Mice and Men*?

5 Which republic occupies the western part of the island of Hispaniola?

6 On which river is the German industrial city of Cologne?

7 Which bowed stringed instrument is the alto of the violin family?

8 What is the derived SI unit of electrical resistance?

9 Which comedian stars in the 1923 silent comedy *Safety Last*?

10 Which Walt Disney film was recreated as a stage musical in London in 1999?

Quiz 141

1 In which country is Lake Wakatipu?

2 In which constellation is the group of stars known as The Plough or The Big Dipper?

3 In the Old Testament, who was the wife of King Ahab?

4 In which century did the English composer and organist Thomas Tallis live?

5 What is the capital of the United Arab Emirates?

6 Which Italian cruise liner was hijacked by the PLO in 1985?

7 Which singer and actress played Evita in the 1996 film of that name?

8 Which pair of aviators made the first non-stop flight across the Atlantic Ocean?

9 What was the name of the songwriting brother of George Gershwin?

10 What is another name for the world's second highest mountain, Godwen Austen?

Quiz 142

1 In 1971, which Canadian folk singer released the international hit *If You Could Read My Mind*?

2 Who won the 2007 World Championship snooker title?

3 Which canine mammal is also known as a prairie wolf?

4 Which order of insects includes bees and wasps?

5 Which blackish mineral is the principal source of radium and uranium?

6 The River Douro in south-west Europe forms part of the border between which two countries?

7 In Greek mythology, which fruit induced forgetfulness in those who ate it?

8 Which town in Umbria, Italy, was the birthplace of St Francis?

9 In which African country is the port of Agadir, which was largely destroyed by an earthquake in 1960?

10 Of what is phytopathology the scientific study?

Quiz 143

1 Christiania is the former name of which European capital city?

2 Which actor directed and starred in the 1983 film *Sudden Impact*?

3 Who was the Roman goddess of the hunt and of the Moon?

4 Which pop singer was born Reginald Dwight?

5 Which husband and wife team created the television puppet series *Thunderbirds*?

6 On which sea is the port of Odessa in Ukraine?

7 What is Eithne Ni Bhraonain's more familiar name?

8 Which Biblical herd ran into the sea and drowned after being driven mad?

9 In which year did Italian fascist dictator Benito Mussolini die?

10 Who composed the soundtrack for the film *Titanic*?

Quiz 144

1 From which country does the band Sigur Ros come?

2 What was the name of the character played by Antonio Fargas in the TV cop show *Starsky and Hutch*?

3 Which common servant is the lover of Columbine in the *Comedia dell'Arte*?

4 In the Old Testament, who was the second son of Adam and Eve?

5 On which river is the Texas city of Laredo?

6 Which country administers the Aleutian Islands?

7 In which US state is the Yosemite National Park?

8 In which South American country is the seaport of Florianopolis?

9 Guernsey, Jersey and Sark are part of which island group?

10 What meat-derived foodstuff did Kenneth Daigneau famously give a name to in 1937?

Quiz 145

1 In which organ of the body is the hippocampus?

2 Which emperor of Japan renounced his divinity and became a constitutional monarch after Japan surrendered at the end of World War II?

3 In Greek mythology, who was the husband of Medea and leader of the Argonauts who sailed in quest of the Golden Fleece?

4 Which two countries are connected by the Simplon Pass?

5 What was the name of the US airbase near the English town of Newbury, where a women's peace camp was set up in 1981?

6 Which hard silvery metal has the chemical symbol Ni?

7 With which of the senses is the word olfactory connected?

8 What name is given to the form of ritual suicide practised by Japanese Samurai?

9 By what letters were the elite German military corps, the Schutzstaffel, known?

10 Which warlike seafaring Biblical people give their name to people indifferent to artistic or cultural values?

Quiz 146

1 Which London landmark came from Heliopolis in Egypt?

2 Which popular Italian operatic tenor made his debut at La Scala in 1966?

3 What name is given to any animal without a backbone?

4 Which spice is obtained from the plant *zingiber officinale*?

5 Which London park contains the Serpentine, Rotten Row and Speakers' Corner?

6 Which is the oldest university in the USA?

7 Which apostle and martyr was originally known as Saul of Tarsus?

8 Of which breed of sledge dog is the Siberian the best known?

9 Which naturally occurring protein that helps to fight viruses was discovered by British virologist Alick Isaacs in 1957?

10 What is the SI unit of intensity of illumination?

Quiz 147

1 In which European country is the town of Neuchâtel?

2 From which ship did the famous bell hanging in the underwriting room at Lloyd's of London come?

3 Of which US city is Beverly Hills a residential suburb?

4 In which European city is the Galileo Galilei airport?

5 Which New Zealand soprano sang at the wedding of the Prince and Princess of Wales?

6 What name is given to the soft tissue found in the cavities of bones?

7 What is the name for the shaggy-coated wild ox which inhabits mountain pastures of central Asia?

8 Which Tuscan city hosts the annual Palio horseraces?

9 What type of tree was Yggdrasil, that was thought to span heaven and hell in Norse mythology?

10 Which rock and roll pioneer wrote *Johnny B Goode* and *Roll Over Beethoven*?

Quiz 148

1 Which Greek poet is traditionally considered to be the inventor of tragedy?

2 What name is given to a mass of soft unconsolidated sand that is unable to support any appreciable weight when saturated?

3 Which three Allied leaders attended the Yalta Conference in 1945?

4 What is the name of the famous geyser in Yellowstone National Park?

5 How many players are there in a netball team?

6 Which Jewish holiday is also known as the Day of Atonement?

7 Which of Shakespeare's great tragedies is set in Elsinore Castle?

8 What is the SI unit of force?

9 Which disease was deliberately introduced into the UK in the 1950s to control the rabbit population?

10 The second atomic bomb used against Japan in World War II was dropped on which port city?

Quiz 149

1 In which country was conductor Andre Previn born?

2 Which ingredient found in tonic water was the first drug used to treat malaria?

3 What name is given to the use in war of toxic substances on humans, animals or plants?

4 What sort of creature is a 'mamba'?

5 Which singer's first big hit was *Heartbreak Hotel*?

6 What sort of creature is a 'grouper'?

7 Of which US state is Atlanta the capital?

8 In Greek mythology, who was the last king of Troy?

9 Which native North American girl saved the life of Captain John Smith?

10 Which prime number is between 11 and 17?

Quiz 150

1 Which hard white substance forms the tusks of elephants and walruses?

2 What name is given to a line on a map joining places of equal temperature?

3 How many horns has an Indian rhinoceros?

4 Which stage of human history came after the Bronze Age?

5 Which French novelist wrote the book translated as *Remembrance of Things Past*?

6 What is the anatomical name for the lower jawbone?

7 In which US state is Las Vegas?

8 What sort of creature is a 'mugger'?

9 Which Scottish mathematician invented logarithms?

10 What do the initials NATO stand for?

Quiz 151

1 Name the walled city in Canada that has been declared a UNESCO World Heritage Site.

2 Which United States film actress (born in Canada) who starred in silent films, was born Gladys Smith?

3 From the Jordanian port of Aqaba, three other countries can be seen: can you name them?

4 Who plays the part of ruthless casino owner Willy Bank in the 2007 film *Ocean's Thirteen*?

5 On a standard typewriter keyboard, which letter lies between the 'Q' and the 'E'?

6 In which part of the body would you find the organ of Corti?

7 Which is closest to the Sun: Jupiter or Pluto?

8 What is the capital of Canada?

9 Which German-born physicist was famous for his theories of relativity?

10 Which Swiss city is the location of the headquarters of the International Red Cross and the World Health Organisation?

Quiz 152

1 What sort of creature is an eland?

2 During the Spanish Civil War, the bombing of which Basque town by German planes inspired a famous painting by Picasso?

3 On which continent is the volcano Mount Erebus?

4 Which Roman soldier and martyr was supposedly sentenced to be executed by archers?

5 Which small prosimian primate of Madagascar has a ring-tailed variety?

6 In which US state is the city of Pittsburgh?

7 Which Roman Catholic order founded by St Angela Merici in 1535 was the first women's teaching order?

8 What name is given to a device in which a moving fluid drives a wheel or motor?

9 Which Old Testament character was banished to the Land of Nod on the east of Eden?

10 In which Hollywood blockbuster did Bruce Willis play an oil-driller attempting to save the world from being destroyed by an asteroid?

Quiz 153

1 What name is given to the rapid movement of snow and ice and sometimes rock debris down a steep slope?

2 Which Italian island was Napoleon's first place of exile?

3 What name is given to vines or shrubs of the genus *lonicera*?

4 Which protein hormone is secreted by the Islets of Langerhans in the pancreas in response to a high concentration of glucose in the blood?

5 What was the former name of the Istanbul suburb of Uskudar, site of Florence Nightingale's hospital in the Crimean War?

6 To which French town was the papacy removed for much of the 14th century?

7 Of which South American country is Asuncion the capital?

8 How many cards are in a standard pack of playing cards (excluding jokers)?

9 Of which country was Shimon Peres prime minister?

10 Which fire-retarding fibrous form of a certain silicate mineral has white and blue varieties?

Quiz 154

1 Which alkaline fluid is produced by the liver and stored in the gall bladder?

2 Which French dramatist wrote *Tartuffe* and *Le Bourgeois Gentilhomme*?

3 The name of which major religion translates as 'submission'?

4 Which important religious building contains the Kaaba?

5 Which opera was composed by Verdi for the opening of the Suez Canal?

6 Who was Lord Protector of England from 1653 to 1658?

7 What was the name of King Arthur's magic sword?

8 Which Russian author wrote the novel *A Month in the Country*?

9 Which singer and songwriter recorded the 1965 album *Highway 61 Revisited*?

10 Who was the last king of Rome?

Quiz 155

1 In Canada, what is the RCMP?

2 By what name is the European freshwater fish *tinca tinca* better known?

3 In which South American country did the ballroom dance the tango originate?

4 Which British dramatist wrote *A Man for all Seasons* and the screenplay for *Lawrence of Arabia*?

5 In which Italian city is the Uffizi Art Gallery, which contains the art treasures of the Medici family?

6 Which syndrome is also called myalgic encephalomyelitis?

7 Which substance used as a form of riot control is also called 'lachrymator'?

8 Which armoured military vehicle was invented by Ernest Swinton?

9 What name is given to the tough fibrous cords that connect muscles to bones?

10 Which is the largest of the Canary Islands?

Quiz 156

1 In which South American country are the ports of Concepción, Valparaíso and Antofagasta?

2 In which country are the Magyars the largest ethnic group?

3 Which four letters often appear on the representation of the cross in Christian art?

4 Who became king of France in the July revolution of 1830?

5 Which of the gifts brought by the three Wise Men to Jesus is also known as olibanum?

6 In Greek mythology, which king was condemned to stand within reach of fruit and water that moved away when he tried to reach for them?

7 Which number system uses only the digits 0 and 1?

8 Which famous cowboy actor and singer was associated with the horse Trigger?

9 Cape Agulhas is the southernmost point of which continent?

10 Which British-born conductor headed the Philadelphia Orchestra from 1912 to 1938 and appeared in Disney's *Fantasia*?

Quiz 157

1 In which US state is the city of Tampa?

2 What is the capital of Jamaica?

3 Who wrote *The Strange Case of Dr Jekyll and Mr Hyde* and *The Master of Ballantrae*?

4 In zoology, which order of mammals includes monkeys, apes and man?

5 For what do the initials ISBN stand?

6 Which form of gelatin is obtained from the swim bladders of various fishes?

7 What sort of creature is a jacamar?

8 Which British rock singer recorded the album *Every Picture Tells a Story*?

9 Which is the world's largest continent?

10 Which noisy black and white member of the crow family is attracted to bright objects?

Quiz 158

1 What name is given to the extensive grasslands of the interior of North America?

2 What name is given to marks on the body of a living person, resembling the wounds that Christ received on the cross?

3 What is the capital city and chief port of Tasmania?

4 Who was the first boxer to beat Muhammad Ali as a professional?

5 Which English artist noted for his pictures of swimming pools was the subject of the 1974 film *A Bigger Splash*?

6 Which Charles Dickens novel features the character Fagin?

7 Which naval administrator is famous for his diary, which includes descriptions of the plague and the Great Fire of London?

8 In Norse mythology, what was the home of the principal gods, linked to Earth by the rainbow bridge Bifrost?

9 Which light silvery white metallic element has the symbol Mg?

10 Who is head of state of Monaco?

ANSWERS:
1 Prairies, 2 Stigmata, 3 Hobart, 4 Joe Frasier, 5 David Hockney, 6 Oliver Twist, 7 Samuel Pepys, 8 Asgard, 9 Magnesium, 10 Prince Albert II.

Quiz 159

1 Which port city can be seen to its best advantage from the top station of the Fløyen mountain railway?

2 What name is given to the extensive grasslands of eastern Russia and Central Asia?

3 Which spectacular cave on the Hebridean island of Staffa inspired the *Hebrides Overture* by Mendelssohn?

4 Who wrote *The Guns of Navarone* and *Where Eagles Dare*?

5 Which US actor starred in the films *The Magnificent Seven*, *Bullitt* and *Papillon*?

6 Do stalagmites grow upwards or downwards?

7 Hilversum is the location of which country's main radio and television broadcasting centre?

8 Which gas used in advertising signs has the symbol Ne?

9 What is the name of the small transverse flute that is accompanied by drums in military bands?

10 Which branch of mathematics uses symbols to represent unknown quantities?

Quiz 160

1 In which year did Hillary and Tenzing become the first mountaineers to reach the summit of Mount Everest?

2 Which is the highest mountain in North America?

3 What is the English name for the movement in French cinema called 'nouvelle vague'?

4 What is the medical name for short-sightedness?

5 Which female aviator established records with solo flights to Australia, Tokyo and the Cape of Good Hope in the 1930s?

6 Which country is surrounded by Austria, Slovakia, Ukraine, Romania, Serbia, Croatia and Slovenia?

7 What is the name of the character who personifies the US government and people?

8 Which acute viral infection passed on by animal bites is also called hydrophobia?

9 Which fortified palace on a rocky hill in Granada is an outstanding example of Moorish architecture?

10 What do the initials UNICEF stand for?

Quiz 161

1 Who directed the films *The Leopard*, *The Damned* and *Death in Venice?*

2 From which plant is Mexican tequila distilled?

3 The childhood disease rickets is caused by a deficiency of which vitamin?

4 Which garden pest is also known as a thunder fly?

5 What name is given to the study and history of words?

6 Which South American soldier and statesman was known as The Liberator?

7 In which South American country is the port of Fray Bentos?

8 Of which African country is Conakry the capital?

9 Which island in the Pacific Ocean was settled by mutineers from the *Bounty* and Tahitian women in 1790?

10 What name is given to an ionised gas produced at extremely high temperature?

Quiz 162

1 Which actress played Scarlett O'Hara in the 1939 film *Gone With the Wind*?

2 Which ski resort is famous for the Cresta Run?

3 What name for an irregular soldier or freedom fighter comes from the Spanish for 'small war'?

4 What is the usual date of the vernal or spring equinox?

5 Which French city is famous for its annual 24-hour race?

6 The disease scurvy is caused by a deficiency of which vitamin?

7 By what name is Swiss-born French architect Charles-Edouard Jeanneret known?

8 What name is given to the placenta when it is expelled following delivery of a baby?

9 What was the first name of Argentinian revolutionary Che Guevara?

10 Which fortified wine takes its name from Jerez de la Frontera, where it was originally made?

Quiz 163

1 How many tentacles has a squid?

2 What was the stage name of actress Harlean Carpentier, the original Blonde Bombshell?

3 Of which fruit is morello a variety?

4 Which Irish novelist, famous for his ghost stores, wrote *Uncle Silas* and *In a Glass Darkly*?

5 Which presidential retreat in the Appalachian Mountains was the venue for peace agreements between Israel and Egypt in the 1970s?

6 What was the nationality of the composer César Franck?

7 Which unorthodox US chess player beat Boris Spassky in Reykjavik in 1972, to become World Champion?

8 What sort of beans are used to make baked beans?

9 By what name is the mouth organ also known?

10 Which rare antelope is the national emblem of South Africa?

Quiz 164

1 In Greek mythology, who was the daughter of Agamemnon who helped her brother Orestes to kill her mother Clytemnestra?

2 Which famous invention did James Hargreaves name after his daughter?

3 In Norse mythology, what was the name of the hall to which the Valkyries carried the bodies of fallen warriors?

4 Which Old Testament character maintained his faith in God, despite losing his family, property and health?

5 In which year did Margaret Thatcher become the first woman prime minister of the United Kingdom?

6 Which Indian city gives its name to a type of riding breeches?

7 What is the capital of Algeria?

8 Which French patriot was otherwise known as the Maid of Orléans?

9 What is the largest city in South Africa?

10 From which Indian Ocean port of call could you visit the Pettah Bazaar and the Cinnamon Gardens?

Quiz 165

1 What name is given to the European blister beetle, once used in powdered form as a supposed aphrodisiac?

2 What is astronaut Buzz Aldrin's real first name?

3 Of which US state is Madison the capital?

4 What nationality was the painter and etcher Paul Klee?

5 Which British spy defected to the Soviet Union in 1951 with Guy Burgess?

6 Which British actress married Laurence Olivier in 1961?

7 In Arthurian legend, what was the name of the wizard who counselled King Arthur?

8 What is the capital of Thailand?

9 What is the innermost planet of the Solar System?

10 What is the name of the official Washington residence of the US president?

Quiz 166

1 Which London street, associated with government offices, contains The Cenotaph?

2 What is the commercial name of the anti-impotence drug developed by Pfizer Labs?

3 Which English author and lexicographer was famous for his *Dictionary*, first published in 1755?

4 Of which territory of Canada, associated with a famous gold-rush, is Whitehorse the capital?

5 Which star cluster in the constellation Taurus is named after the seven daughters of Atlas?

6 Of which African country was Hastings Banda named President for Life in 1971?

7 What name was given to Roman citizens who did not belong to the privileged class of the Patricians?

8 What was the name of the programme of social reform pursued by President Harry S Truman?

9 Which British financial institution was founded in 1694?

10 Which port and resort in North Yorkshire, England, has associations with Captain Cook and Bram Stoker's *Dracula*?

Quiz 167

1 If it were possible to sail due north from the north coast of Scotland (the Arctic ice being your only barrier!) in which country would you make landfall?

2 The name of which alcoholic drink is derived from the Gaelic 'uisge beatha', meaning 'the water of life'?

3 After which English scientist is the SI unit of electrical capacitance, the farad, named?

4 By what name was blues and folk singer Huddie Ledbetter known?

5 What sort of creature is a sea butterfly?

6 What name is given to the movement for reunification of the various branches of the Christian church?

7 By what name was Scottish King Robert I known?

8 Which city is known as Firenze to the Italians?

9 Who wrote the music to the operas *The Marriage of Figaro* and *Don Giovanni*?

10 Which term translates as 'lightning war' and was used to describe military tactics used by Germany in World War II?

Quiz 168

1 Which sign of the zodiac is represented by a bull?

2 What word for 'killer' is derived from the Arabic for 'hashish-eaters'?

3 In Greek mythology, who was the muse of comedy?

4 Which German city, famous as the site of the Krupp steelworks, is the administrative centre of the Ruhr?

5 Which US novelist wrote *Slaughterhouse Five* and *Breakfast of Champions*?

6 Which peninsula of Western Asia forms the greater part of the Asian portion of Turkey?

7 Of which country did Hosni Mubarak become president in 1981?

8 The Norsemen who raided much of Europe from about 800AD were known by what name?

9 What name is given to swollen and twisted veins, especially in the legs?

10 What is the capital of Scotland?

Quiz 169

1 Who was the god of thunder in Norse mythology?

2 Which French composer wrote *Boléro* and the ballet *Daphnis et Chloë*?

3 Of which African country is Asmara the capital?

4 Which monastery and palace near Madrid, built for Philip II, houses a famous art collection?

5 What name was given to the Chinese students organised to eliminate revisionism during the Cultural Revolution?

6 In which European country is the North Sea port of Esbjerg?

7 Which leading Nazi rocket engineer was taken to the US after World War II and worked for NASA?

8 What is the judicial capital of South Africa?

9 Which Oxfordshire mansion was a gift from Queen Anne to the Duke of Marlborough and the birthplace of Winston Churchill?

10 What name is given to horses bred for racing that are descended from three Arab stallions brought into England?

Quiz 170

1 Which Canadian actor is the father of Kiefer Sutherland?

2 Which continent comprises the land around the South Pole?

3 What name is given to a stoat in its white winter coat?

4 Which Norwegian explorer beat Scott's expedition to the South Pole in 1911?

5 Who wrote the detective novels *Murder on the Orient Express* and *Death on the Nile*?

6 What name is given to a shrub or tree trained to grow flat against a wall or a trellis?

7 Which actor starred in the films *All the President's Men* and *Out of Africa*?

8 What was the nationality of author Laurens van der Post?

9 Who wrote the autobiographical work *Goodbye to All That*?

10 Which Bavarian town is famous for its Passion Play which is performed every ten years?

Quiz 171

1 What was the name of the driver of the car in which Diana, Princess of Wales, was killed?

2 Which light gas is used for inflating airships and balloons?

3 In which year did Elizabeth II become Queen?

4 What name is given to an area of desert where water is available?

5 What is the capital of The Netherlands?

6 Which Shakespeare play features the character Shylock?

7 Which radioactive metallic element has the symbol Th?

8 Which British naturalist, writer and zoo curator penned *My Family and Other Animals*?

9 Which is the world's largest inland sea?

10 What name is given to the rounded underground base of the stem of a daffodil, tulip or onion?

Quiz 172

1 From which ocean into which other ocean would one pass going east past the Cape of Good Hope?

2 In which country is the port city of Casablanca?

3 Which US sharpshooter, who performed in Buffalo Bill's *Wild West Show*, inspired the musical *Annie Get Your Gun*?

4 In Greek mythology, whose elopement with Paris precipitated the Trojan War?

5 Which US president came from a family of peanut farmers?

6 By what name was Haitian president François Duvalier better known?

7 Which soft fabric is made from the undercoat of the Kashmir goat?

8 What name is given to a substance that cannot be broken down into simpler fragments by chemical means?

9 Which English navigator was set adrift by a mutinous crew in the Canadian bay which now bears his name?

10 Which Armenian composer wrote the ballets *Gayaneh*, *Spartacus* and *Maskarade*?

Quiz 173

1 By what name are the Royal Botanic Gardens in Surrey, England, known?

2 Which queen of England was known as The Virgin Queen?

3 Who was the sixth wife of King Henry VIII of England?

4 In which sport do riders compete on dirt-tracks using motorcycles without brakes?

5 What was the name of the child (her first) born to Madonna on 14 October 1996?

6 In which former Crown Colony did EOKA fight for independence from Britain?

7 For which vinyl resin is PVA an abbreviation?

8 In which European country is the city of Antwerp?

9 The painter Domenikos Theotokopoulos is better known by which name?

10 The khamsin wind, which blows over Egypt, comes from which desert?

Quiz 174

1 Which fabric used especially for military uniforms gets its name from a Hindi word meaning 'dust-coloured'?

2 What is the name of the small flap that prevents food and fluid from entering the windpipe?

3 What name is given to the compilation of dictionaries?

4 Who was the leader of the Gunpowder Plot?

5 Which US track and field athlete won four gold medals at the 1984 Olympics?

6 Of which European country was Enver Hoxha leader from 1954 to 1985?

7 Which specialized agency of the United Nations is known by the initials WHO?

8 Who was the Greek goddess of love, identified with the Roman goddess Venus?

9 What colour is a female blackbird?

10 In Egyptian mythology, what was the name of the jackal-headed god of the dead?

Quiz 175

1 Of which group of peoples was Arnakuagsak the goddess responsible for ensuring hunters were able to catch enough food and that people remained healthy and strong?

2 By what initials was the Committee of State Security Secret Police of the Soviet Union known?

3 Which religious leader issued the fatwa against Salman Rushdie because of his book *Satanic Verses*?

4 Which of the Apollo space missions made the first manned lunar landing?

5 Which important vitamin is also called ascorbic acid?

6 By what name is an elk known in North America?

7 Which metallic element has the symbol Rh?

8 Which legendary Trojan leader is the hero of Virgil's most famous work?

9 What was the surname of the British royal family until it was changed to Windsor in 1917?

10 What name is given to an industry in which the market is supplied by only one supplier?

Quiz 176

1 Which Austrian city, twice the venue for the Winter Olympics, is the capital of the province of Tirol?

2 Which US novelist wrote *The Bostonians* and *The Turn of the Screw*?

3 What sort of creature is a mandrill?

4 Which Thracian gladiator led a revolt against Rome in 73BC?

5 By what name is propanone, used as a solvent in nail varnish remover, more commonly known?

6 What ancient name is given to the land between the Tigris and Euphrates rivers in present-day Iraq?

7 Which city on the River Vienne is the centre of the French porcelain industry?

8 How many teeth has the normal human adult?

9 Which city replaced Rio de Janeiro as the capital of Brazil in 1960?

10 Which sweet yellow liqueur, consisting of brandy and eggs, originated in The Netherlands?

Quiz 177

1 Which section of the Mediterranean Sea contains the Cyclades and Dodecanese Islands?

2 What name is given to the rate of upward change of the velocity of a moving body?

3 Which English crime writer created Lord Peter Wimsey?

4 What was the ancient name for the Dardanelles, the straits separating European and Asian Turkey?

5 In Greek mythology, which daughter of Demeter was carried off by Hades, who made her queen of the underworld?

6 Who wrote the novel *The Cruel Sea*, based on his own experiences in World War II?

7 Which US president was assassinated by John Wilkes Booth?

8 Which entrepreneur founded the Virgin Record Company in 1969?

9 What name is given to a precipitation that has absorbed sulphur dioxide and nitrogen oxides from the atmosphere?

10 What sort of creature is a hairstreak?

Quiz 178

1 What is the second planet from the sun?

2 Of which Caribbean country is Port-au-Prince the capital?

3 What name is given to the wind pattern that brings heavy rain to south Asia from April to September?

4 In which US state is the volcano Mount St Helen's?

5 What is fermented to make the Japanese drink known as sake?

6 By what name was Russian Tsar Peter I known?

7 Which breed of tail-less short-haired cat was originally bred on the Isle of Man?

8 Which European country was ruled by Antonio de Oliveira Salazar from 1932 to 1968?

9 Which region of the USA comprises the states of Maine, New Hampshire, Vermont, Massachusetts, Rhode Island and Connecticut?

10 Which five-line form of comic verse was popularised by Edward Lear in the 19th century?

Quiz 179

1 Which former Chilean dictator was arrested in London in 1998?

2 What do the initials OPEC stand for?

3 Which Shakespeare play features the characters Mercutio and Tybalt?

4 Which Dutch artist painted *The Anatomy Lesson of Doctor Tulp* and *The Night Watch*?

5 In which US state is the city of San Diego?

6 Which New Testament apostle was martyred on an X-shaped cross?

7 What name is given to the stiffening of a body after death?

8 Who was the Greek goddess of war and wisdom?

9 Which island country was formerly known as the Malagasy Republic?

10 What is the official language of the principality of Liechtenstein?

Quiz 180

1 Which island boasts the Dettifoss and Gullfoss waterfalls and the Hekla volcano?

2 Which country lies between Estonia and Lithuania?

3 Which French sculptor is famous for works such as *The Kiss* and *The Thinker*?

4 Which adult male singing voice is lower than tenor and higher than bass?

5 Approximately how long is the Great Wall of China: is it 1400 miles, 1500 miles or 1600 miles?

6 Which Turkish city was formerly known as Byzantium and Constantinople?

7 To which famous literary figure was Anne Hathaway married?

8 What was the name of the wife of Odysseus, who remained faithful during his long absence?

9 From which former province of Spain did Cervantes' Don Quixote come?

10 Which former Spice Girl was appointed as a Goodwill Ambassador for the UN Population Fund?

Quiz 181

1 What was the Roman name for London?

2 Which Christmas carol concerns the plants *ilex aquifolium and hedera helix*?

3 By what name was Yugoslav President Josip Broz known?

4 On which of the Iles de Salut of French Guiana was Alfred Dreyfuss imprisoned?

5 What sort of creature is a devil's coach-horse?

6 Which non-metallic element has the symbol I?

7 What was the popular name for Ronald Reagan's Strategic Defense Initiative?

8 Of which small Mediterranean island country is Valletta the capital?

9 In which year did the Titanic sink on its maiden voyage?

10 In Greek mythology, by what name were the giant children of Uranus and Gaea known?

Quiz 182

1 Which eye disease is marked by increased pressure within the eye?

2 What was the name of the London restaurant launched by models Claudia Schiffer, Naomi Campbell and Elle MacPherson?

3 Which coastal village in Cornwall has the ruins of a castle reputed to be that of the court of King Arthur?

4 Which Irish-American dancer and choreographer came to fame in *River Dance* and *Lord of the Dance*?

5 What was the name of the royal dynasty of France from 1328 to 1589?

6 Lake Titicaca lies in which two South American countries?

7 Which Scottish band recorded the album *The Man Who*?

8 Which Jewish initiation ceremony takes its name from the Hebrew for 'son of the Commandment'?

9 Which tree's leaves provide the staple diet of koala bears?

10 Which sugar is also known as dextrose or grape sugar?

185

Quiz 183

1 What was the nickname of the German World War I pilot Manfred von Richthofen?

2 Which former British liner is a tourist attraction at Long Beach, California?

3 Which small marine crustaceans are the principal food of whales?

4 Which US guitarist and singer who died in 1970 had a hit with *Purple Haze*?

5 In Greek mythology, who was the daughter of King Priam, whose prophesies were not believed?

6 What sort of creature is a klipspringer?

7 Which word for the citadel of any Russian city was once synonymous with the Soviet government?

8 Which king of Judaea ordered the Massacre of the Innocents?

9 What nationality was the surrealist painter René Magritte?

10 Which Roman Catholic order of friars is known as the Black Friars?

Quiz 184

1 Which Canadian country singer had a No 1 hit in 1970 with *Snowbird*?

2 Which country was divided at the 38th parallel after World War II?

3 Which large German howitzer used in World War I was named after the wife of Gustav Krupp?

4 Which strait separates the South American mainland from Tierre del Fuego?

5 Who was the legendary lover of Hero, who swam across the Hellespont each night?

6 Of which Italian range of mountains is Marmolada the highest peak?

7 In which city is the Dome of the Rock?

8 Which actor starred in the films *The Graduate*, *Midnight Cowboy* and *Tootsie*?

9 Who was crowned Holy Roman Emperor by Pope Leo III in the year 800?

10 What name is given to the study of ancient organisms from fossil remains?

Quiz 185

1 Which Australian medical service began in Cloncurry in Queensland in 1928?

2 Which is the nearest star to Earth?

3 What is the name of the famous ghost ship seen in bad weather off the Cape of Good Hope?

4 Which British-born South African financier had an African country named after him?

5 In which Scottish town was the Royal and Ancient Golf Club founded in 1754?

6 What is the name for the flame-like electrical discharge that sometimes occurs above ship's masts in thundery weather?

7 Of which Canadian province is St John's the capital?

8 What is the medical name for the tube (also called the gullet) by which food travels from the mouth to the stomach?

9 Which French novelist and aviator wrote *The Little Prince*?

10 Which city in Florida is closest to the Walt Disney World complex?

Quiz 186

1 What sort of labour-saving device was patented by Isaac Merrit Singer in 1851?

2 Which Ukrainian town was the site of a nuclear reactor explosion in 1986?

3 What name is given to vegetarians who will not eat any food of animal origin whatsoever?

4 Transylvania is a part of which eastern European country?

5 Which skin condition is also known as hives and nettle rash?

6 At the foot of which famous mountain is the Swiss ski resort of Zermatt?

7 What name is given to a blade that can be attached to the muzzle of a firearm?

8 Which men's athletics competition consists of ten events over two days?

9 Who wrote *The Spy Who Came In From the Cold* and *A Small Town in Germany*?

10 Which US science fiction writer founded the Church of Scientology?

Quiz 187

1 Which of the knights of the Round Table had an adulterous affair with Guinevere?

2 What is the largest island in the Mediterranean Sea?

3 In the Old Testament, which city was captured by Joshua when its walls fell at the blast of the Israelites' trumpets?

4 Which famous battle is known as Custer's Last Stand?

5 What are the names of Shakespeare's *Two Gentlemen of Verona*?

6 In which film did Peter Sellers play the US president, an ex-Nazi scientist and a British RAF officer?

7 The Monument in London was designed by Sir Christopher Wren to commemorate which event of 1666?

8 What was the name of the state council of ancient Rome?

9 What was the name of the principal legislative assembly of Russia from 1906 to 1917?

10 What type of Spanish music and dance was developed by Andalusian gypsies?

Quiz 188

1 Moldova lies between which two countries?

2 Who composed the music for the ballet *Romeo and Juliet* which was first performed in 1938?

3 Which court painter to King Henry VIII of England designed the woodcut series *The Dance of Death*?

4 Which red supergiant is the second largest star in the constellation Orion?

5 With which musical instrument was Andrés Segovia associated?

6 Which South American herb is used to make a treatment for digestive disorders and is commonly used as a flavouring in cocktails?

7 After a life of conquering and terrorising much of Europe, what mundane event led to the death of Attila the Hun?

8 Who was the Swedish naturalist who founded the scientific nomenclature for animals and plants?

9 In Greek mythology, what was the name of the king whose touch turned everything into gold?

10 What name is given to a long narrow sea inlet lying between steep mountain slopes?

Quiz 189

1 Who was the mother of Liza Minnelli?

2 Which English river flows through Newcastle, Gateshead and Jarrow?

3 Which unit of distance is equal to the mean distance from the Earth to the Sun?

4 Of which country was Mohammed Riza Pahlavi the shah until 1979?

5 What name was given to the military alliance between the Soviet Union and East European states signed in 1955?

6 In Hinduism, what name is given to the sum of one's actions carried forward from one life to the next?

7 Which of the apostles refused to believe in the resurrection until he had seen Christ?

8 Which US dancer, singer and actor was born Frederick Austerlitz?

9 Which German town is famous for its castle which was used as a high-security POW camp in World War II?

10 Who wrote the play *Rosencrantz & Guildenstern Are Dead*?

Quiz 190

1 By what name is the clavicle usually known?

2 With which visual art movement is US Roy Lichtenstein associated?

3 Which Irish village is famous for its castle, which has a stone that is kissed to give the power of persuasive speech?

4 Which savage Scandinavian warrior's name means 'bear shirts'?

5 Black water fever is a serious complication of which infectious disease?

6 Rock crystal is a transparent colourless form of which mineral?

7 Which US aviator and entrepreneur became a recluse from 1950 until his death in 1976?

8 What name for a traitor is derived from a Norwegian who collaborated with the Nazis during World War II?

9 Which widely cultivated cereal grass is also known as Indian Corn?

10 Who plays the part of Abigail Sponder in the 2007 film *Ocean's Thirteen*?

Quiz 191

1 Which four herbs feature in the English folksong *Scarborough Fair*?

2 Which book by Jules Verne tells of the adventures of Phileas Fogg and his servant Passepartout?

3 Which green vegetable features in the Indian dish of sag aloo?

4 Which colour comes before green in the colours of the rainbow?

5 Which country is the world's largest producer of cheese?

6 Mimas is a moon of which planet?

7 How many humps has a bactrian camel?

8 If 25 September falls on a Monday, on which day will Christmas Day fall in that same year?

9 On a standard typewriter keyboard, which letter lies between the 'B' and the 'M'?

10 Who plays the part of Jack Burden, a journalist, in the 2006 film *All The King's Men* based on the Robert Penn Warren novel of the same name?

Quiz 192

1 Which US awards are given annually in the fields of journalism, literature and musical composition?

2 What is the name of the brown pigment made from the ink of cuttlefish?

3 What is the most southerly point of South America?

4 Which constellation includes Sirius, the brightest star in the night sky?

5 In South African politics, what do the initials ANC stand for?

6 What was the legendary capital of King Arthur's kingdom?

7 Which region of Canada comprises the districts of Mackenzie, Keewatin and Franklin?

8 What name is given to the study of the behaviour and flow of air around objects?

9 What name is given to the condition of having an abnormally low body temperature, often associated with elderly people?

10 What name is given to the proportion of water vapour in the atmosphere?

Quiz 193

1 Which light volcanic rock derived from acidic lava is used as an abrasive?

2 Which European peninsula is occupied by Spain and Portugal?

3 Which extinct snow-topped Tanzanian volcano is the highest mountain in Africa?

4 What name is given to the art of producing miniature trees by selective pruning?

5 Which keyboard instrument was invented by Bartolomeo Christofori?

6 The Arthur Ashe Stadium is the main stadium at which US tennis centre?

7 What was the capital of West Germany from 1949 to 1990?

8 ...and what is the capital of the united Germany?

9 What is the traditional costume of Japan, still used by women for formal wear?

10 What sort of creature is an ibex?

Quiz 194

1 Which wading bird was revered by the ancient Egyptians as a symbol of the god Thoth?

2 On what date is Independence Day celebrated in the USA?

3 What name is given to a well sunk into an aquifer in which water rises under its own pressure?

4 Which Roman general abandoned his wife Octavia to live with Cleopatra in Egypt?

5 What is the name of the collection of ancient Egyptian manuscripts buried with mummies as a guide to the afterlife?

6 Which king of England was married to Margaret of Anjou?

7 Which park to the west of Paris contains Longchamp Racecourse?

8 The Crimea Peninsula is part of which European country?

9 Who became Archduchess of Austria and Queen of Hungary in 1740?

10 What is the most famous novel by James Fenimore Cooper?

Quiz 195

1 Which is the chief island of the Society Islands in French Polynesia?

2 Mount Cook is the highest mountain of which nation in the South Pacific?

3 What name is given to an agent which causes cancer?

4 What sort of creature is a margay?

5 Which US silversmith was famous for his night ride to warn the people of Massachusetts of the approach of British troops?

6 Which item of clothing is named after the officer who led the Charge of the Light Brigade in the Crimean War?

7 Of which country is Margrethe II the reigning queen?

8 Which prophetic book is the last in the New Testament?

9 Which French mime artiste was best known for his white-faced character Bip?

10 Which reed-like plant was used by the ancient Egyptians to make paper?

Quiz 196

1 Which English dramatist and poet was killed in a tavern brawl in Deptford in 1593?

2 What name is given to the transfer of heat within a fluid by means of motion of the fluid?

3 Vienna and Belgrade lie on the banks of which great European river?

4 Which effect is responsible for the apparent change in pitch of a siren as a vehicle approaches and then recedes?

5 The hull of which Tudor warship was raised from the seabed and placed in dry dock in Portsmouth in 1982?

6 Which Greek philosopher was tutor to Alexander the Great?

7 In which 1805 battle was Admiral Horatio Nelson mortally wounded?

8 Which British singer died in 1999 on the day she was due to go to Buckingham Palace to receive her OBE?

9 Who were the parents of Cain and Abel?

10 Who played the rôle of Holly in the 2006 film *Scary Movie 4* and Candy in the 2007 film *I Want Candy*?

Quiz 197

1 What is the capital of Argentina?

2 In 1845, who invented a process which revolutionised the production of steel?

3 Which arm of the Mediterranean Sea lies between Italy and the Balkan Peninsula?

4 Which novel by H G Wells is partly set in the year 802701?

5 In which garden near Jerusalem was Jesus betrayed by Judas Iscariot?

6 In which US state is the city of Omaha?

7 Which North American river is the chief tributary of the Mississippi?

8 Which Nazi leader was arrested when he made a secret trip to Scotland in 1941 in an attempt to negotiate peace?

9 Which is closest to the Sun: the Earth or Mars?

10 Who provides the voice of Artie in the 2007 film *Shrek the Third*?

Quiz 198

1 Which Chilean island, famous for its giant stone sculptures, is also called Rapa Nui?

2 Which actress is the elder sister of Warren Beatty?

3 What was Thomas Twyford's gift to civilization with his invention of 1885?

4 Which US inventor developed the first safety lift?

5 What is the minimum number of tennis strokes a player needs to make to win a set?

6 Which English poet wrote *Paradise Lost* and *Paradise Regained*?

7 Which rare Indonesian monitor lizard is the largest living lizard?

8 What was the name of the raft used by Thor Heyerdahl on his 1947 expedition?

9 In 1947, which country was created as a separate state for the Muslim minority in India?

10 Diplodocus and triceratops are examples of what kind of creature?

Quiz 199

1 To which country's stock exchange does the DAX index belong?

2 In which African country is the city of Timbuktu?

3 What does the Latin phrase 'mea culpa' mean?

4 What name is given to the band of light crossing the night sky, composed of innumerable stars that are too faint to be seen individually?

5 Which bacteriologist has been credited with the discovery of the antibiotic penicillin?

6 Which two balloonists were the first to circumnavigate the globe?

7 How many days after the Resurrection is Christ said to have ascended into heaven?

8 Who was chancellor of West Germany from 1969 to 1974 and winner of the 1971 Nobel Peace Prize?

9 Which unit used to express depths of water is equal to six feet?

10 Which city in Massachusetts is the seat of Harvard University?

Quiz 200

1 Who played the part of Woody Stevens in the 2007 film *Wild Hogs*?

2 The malleus, incus, and stapes are all bones found in which part of the body?

3 Of which Eastern European country was Nicolae Ceausescu president?

4 Which US explorer was the first man to reach the North Pole?

5 By what name is a plant of the genus *digitalis* commonly known?

6 In which European country is the cathedral city of Breda?

7 Which beetle takes its name from its well-developed mandibles that resemble antlers?

8 *Death of a Princess*, a TV drama based on a real event caused a diplomatic row between Britain and which country in 1980?

9 Which Greek island exploded in 1650 BC and probably resulted in the extinction of the Minoan civilisation?

10 Which German battleship was sunk on 27 May 1941 on what was to be her only voyage?

Quiz 201

1 What kind of books does the specialist publisher Baedeker produce?

2 What name is given to the indigenous Polynesian people of New Zealand?

3 What name is given to the leader of congregational prayer in a mosque?

4 Invented by Leo Baekeland, what was the first plastic?

5 Which island in San Francisco Bay was the site of a notorious maximum security prison?

6 What was Antonio Stradivari famous for manufacturing?

7 Which is the largest island in the Canadian Arctic?

8 What name is given to an abnormally low concentration of sugar in the blood?

9 What name is given to rodents of the family *sciuridae*?

10 What name is given to the hereditary condition in which blood does not clot properly?

Quiz 202

1 The philanthropist and industrialist Andrew Carnegie was born in which country?

2 The year 1959 saw the start of which record label in the US city of Detroit?

3 What was the nickname of the runner Paavo Nurmi?

4 Of which African country is Colonel Gaddafi head of state?

5 What are Nova Scotia, New Brunswick and Prince Edward Island collectively known as?

6 Which prolific US inventor devised the gramophone, which he called the phonograph?

7 In which country is the town of Delft, famous for its pottery and porcelain?

8 Who was the first African president of the International Cricket Council, who died in Cape Town in May 2007, at the age of 57?

9 What is the name of the branch of law related to ships and shipping?

10 What name is given to exercises, often performed to music, designed to improve the physique?

Quiz 203

1 The Egyptian god Apis took the form of which animal?

2 What is the highest number on a roulette wheel?

3 In which African country did the Coptic church originate?

4 Who scored England's only try when they beat Australia 20-17 in the 2003 Rugby World Cup final in Sydney?

5 By what name is the plant *solanum tuberosum*, introduced into England by Sir Walter Raleigh, better known?

6 Which highly venomous snake can extend its neck ribs to form a hood?

7 Which instrument in an aircraft measures height above sea level?

8 Which metallic element has the symbol K?

9 By what abbreviation is polyvinyl chloride better known?

10 In horticulture, what name is given to the propagation method in which part of one plant is transferred onto another?

Quiz 204

1 Which US novelist created the detective Philip Marlowe?

2 Which Swiss resort on Lake Geneva hosts an annual television festival which awards a Golden Rose?

3 From which European language is the South African 'Afrikaans' derived?

4 On which New York island are Broadway, Wall Street and Central Park?

5 Which coastal region on the Adriatic Sea gives its name to a dog with a spotted coat?

6 Which US comedienne and actress was born Caryn Johnson?

7 Which rock star was born Gordon Sumner?

8 In which country was Britain's adopted tennis player Greg Rusedski born?

9 Which warm, dry wind is named after the North American native word for 'snow-eater'?

10 What was the name of the ship belonging to the environmental pressure group Greenpeace, which was sunk by French intelligence agents?

Quiz 205

1 What was the name of the plane which dropped the atomic bomb on Hiroshima?

2 From which disease did tenor Jose Carreras recover, to resume his career in 1988?

3 At which Pacific port does the Trans-Siberian Railway terminate?

4 Which is the smallest state of the USA?

5 In the UK, which Roman frontier was 73 miles long and ran from Wallsend-on-Tyne in the east to Bowness on the Solway Firth in the west?

6 In which country was tennis player Martina Navratilova born?

7 Which constellation takes its name from the Latin for 'swan'?

8 What nationality was the psychiatrist Sigmund Freud?

9 Which US poet and critic broadcast fascist propoganda during World War II?

10 What name is given to the group of underwater plateaus south-east of Newfoundland, around which are the richest fishing grounds in the world?